Sense in a
Clear Bottle

Sense in a Clear Bottle

By
Memuna Sillah

AFRICA WORLD PRESS

TRENTON | LONDON | CAPE TOWN | NAIROBI | ADDIS ABABA | ASMARA | IBADAN | NEW DELHI

AFRICA WORLD PRESS
541 West Ingham Avenue | Suite B
Trenton, New Jersey 08638

Book design: Dawid Kahts
Cover design: Ashraful Haque

Cataloging-in-Publication Data may be obtained from the Library of Congress.

ISBNs: 9781569027998 (HB)
        9781569028001 (PB)

For
Papa and Attatie

Table of Contents

Prologue

"If you have a Marabou name, do not apply to these schools." It was my final year at Holy Trinity School. Mrs. Harding was guiding us through the grueling process of secondary school entrance. She wrote the names on the blackboard: *Annie Walsh Memorial Secondary School, Methodist Girls High School, St. Joseph's Convent Secondary School.*

I had Marabou names; Memuna Mameh Sillah—but I ignored her.

We had made promises; Barbara Samuel, Joy Decker, Frederika Thomas, and I, that our friendship would continue into Annie Walsh Memorial School. We would eat lunch together, our uniforms starched.

It was a marker-upper moment for us. If you failed the Common Entrance Exams, you likely became an elementary school dropout. If you passed, you prayed a good school wanted you. Otherwise, you'd find yourself in a school where girls get pregnant, and you brought your own chair.

"Listen to me," Mrs. Harding shouted over the classroom chatter. She wrote, *Oshora School,* under the other three schools. "You should be able to get into Oshora School."

Fredericka pulled on Joy's ponytail. Barbara snatched my pencil. I threw bits of cut-up papers on everyone's face, and I completed my form, just as I had intended.

The teacher's high heels clanked on the cement floor between our desks.

"Annie Walsh School!" Her chunky hand was on Barbara's form. "Well, you are Parson Samuel's granddaughter, after all." She moved to Fredericka's desk. "My mother is an old girl of Annie Walsh School."

1

Fredericka was apologetic, even though she did not have a Marabou name. Mrs. Harding straightened up, put her hands on her waist and feigned alarm.

"How come I never knew that?"

Fredericka relaxed with a smile.

Then Joy held her ponytail end between two fingers and bragged, "My mother, too, is an old girl."

I could say my parents had already met with the principal and secured me a place. I could say, I'll do so well on the exams that the school will have no choice but to accept me. Or I could lean back in my chair, pull on the tail of my braids and lie, *My mother, too, is an old girl*. What I will never say, is that my mother did not even complete elementary school.

"I know what's best for each one of you." Mrs. Harding was now tracing her finger on my form.

The classroom noise had abated, now that every girl was expecting the teacher around her desk soon. So I covered my mouth and talked into Mrs. Harding's neck.

"My mother will call Pa," I whispered. "He'll tell us what to do to get into Annie Walsh School."

The teacher's head twitched, like a young lizard.

"What?" She straightened and threw her hands on her waist. "These girls here are going to Annie Walsh School because their parents have connections with the school."

Full-blown exasperation was apparent in her voice. Her high chest rose and fell.

The pencil began to slip from my hand. Girls had stopped writing. Everyone was staring.

Joy was stifling a chuckle. "You have a Marabou name, and your parents have no connection with the school."

The words were like a drill into a decade-old mold of clay. It demolished my fairytale house.

"My parents will kill the largest sheep there is at Cowyard," I said with the confidence of a sorcerer's daughter.

The suppressed giggles exploded into fits of guffaw.

"My mother will make a big offering!" I did not care who heard me. "I will be accepted into Annie Walsh School."

***

My mother had prepared me for the exams with full-body sweating. I sat naked to my panties in front of a paraffin lamp and a steaming caldron.

"Tell Pa the name of the exam," she ordered.

"It is the Common Entrance Exams," I whispered.

Pa nodded. He was stringy and solemn, and he carried a bulky raffia bag over his dingy kaftan. I was sure Pa had never set foot in a classroom, but the slow, thoughtful way his eyelids fell, and the hand on his chin as he released a deep "Hmm," supported my eleven-year-old conclusion that he understood the importance of school. Besides, anyone acquainted with my mother had to have been imbibed with the information necessary to give great value to the word *school*.

"Give him the name of the school you want to go to," my mother said.

In contrast to Pa's serene ease, and my docile manner, my mother was combat ready. As she spoke, her pupils surged like bullets from the depths of her dark eyes. It was time to buck up, I thought, if only to avoid an unwanted reminder. For my own good, of course.

"I want to go to Annie Walsh School," I said with boldness.

My mother had set up the backyard before Pa arrived: a stack of split wood against the kitchen sink, three firestones beside the kitchen steps, and medicinal leaves shooting out of the rim of a cast iron cauldron.

Pa drifted around the yard, a finger on his chin, like someone contemplating a math problem.

"You have the match?" He pulled the raffia bag over his stained skull cap.

While my mother leaped to the pantry, Pa shoved his cap inside the bag, pulled out a small knife, and settled the bag on the graveled ground. He picked up pieces of wood with the same ease with which he spoke. Shaved off wood chunks and threw the bark in the middle of the fire pit.

Attatie returned with a pint of kerosene in one hand, a matchbox in the other. On her head she carried parcels of bed sheets. Pa got the fire going, then went down to his knees, hands flat on the ground, and put his mouth between the stones to blow wind into the pit.

Meanwhile, my attention was focused, with great panic, for signs of movement in the neighbor's yard. If Josiah came out to use the toilet, he would see me in my underwear, next to this paraphernalia of up-country life. As much as I wanted to pass the exams and go to Annie Walsh School, I would have preferred being indoors while doing homework—like Josiah, like my Christian friends at school. Telling Attatie what I really wanted, though, would have reduced me to a bleating sheep surrounded by women waiting in front of a large pot of hot oil.

I sat on a kitchen bench. Attatie pulled several blankets over my head, then opened my legs to make way for the froth-spitting cauldron. Hot medicinal needles pricked my pupils. My pores drank arid fumes and spilled bitter potion. Sweat dropped from the curves of my panties. I felt bloated all over.

"Pray to Allah." My mother's voice punctured through the covering. "Pray that you do well in your exams," she cried. "Pray that the principals of good schools favor you."

I felt like a piece of meat in hot water, but I could not resist the orders.

"Allah—" I stopped to stifle the bitter vapor descending the walls of my throat.

"Did you hear what I said?" Attatie's knuckles tapped on the blanket over my head. "Don't waste my money," she snapped. "I want you to pray."

I tightened my eyelids and shuffled for distance between me and the pit. It didn't help. In addition to the burning in my eyes and the dry congestion in my throat, the medicinal air had formed a parapet over my nostrils. It had blocked the door to my mind.

I was about to abandon all effort to breathe, when a rush of cold air surged through the dark space, and I began to shiver like a newborn.

"I didn't hear you pray." Attatie removed the blanket.

My eyes were still dim.

"It was very hot," I said, "but I prayed a bit."

"Do you want to go to a good school or not?" She was holding one end of the cauldron as she helped Pa return it to the fire stones.

While Pa went to work getting the fire up again, my mother lectured me.

"You must pray so Allah will help you. This is our way. It is the only way I can help you."

Attatie had learned that the principal of Annie Walsh School was a cantankerous woman. But there was hardly a problem on this earth she did not believe Pa could oust.

She motioned to Pa, and they settled the pot back in front of me and covered me up again with the blankets. Green froth cascaded over the cauldron's frame. The old man's stringy hand snaked inside of the dark space and removed the cauldron cover. This time, I had closed my eyes before the cover came off, and I was better at alternating my breathing between nose and mouth.

When my mother said, "Pray that you do not witness Mrs. Forster's cantankerous half," I was ready. I prayed for the principal's favors. I even summoned, as my mother usually did, the help of my departed grandparents for the exams. Then I gave Allah a list of information I wanted transmitted to the principal.

"Tell Mrs. Forster that Barbara, Joy, and Frederika also want to come to her school. Tell her we will all behave ourselves and do well in class. Tell her we all helped raise money for Trinity School's new parsonage, and we attended the Thanksgiving service.

I was so consumed in the dictation of my message that I did not feel the heat soar when Pa snaked his hand inside the covers again to turn over the hot leaves. It was not until a cold breeze swelled my pores that I jerked back.

"You're ready for the exams now," the old man said, my skin squeaking under the pressure of his index finger. "Your mind is now quick, like a leopard." He waved a wrinkled finger in my face. "You will pass the exam."

My mother ordered me to answer by saying *Ameena*.

"Ameena." I shivered under the midnight breeze.

"And you will go to that school." Pa didn't trust himself with the words *Annie Walsh Memorial School*.

That night, I found myself sitting in a foggy classroom with the usual noise that said a teacher was not present. Then out of nowhere, Mrs. Harding appeared in the doorway. I seemed to have been the only one who saw her, so I waved my hands in the air to warn the class. By fits and starts, everyone noticed her, and the class quieted. But as I turned back to the door, expecting to see her entering the classroom, the space where she had been standing was empty. I turned back to my classmates, and they, too, had vanished. I was alone in the room, trapped in a fog that suddenly darkened.

In the morning, I said nothing of the dream to my mother. I was afraid it would upset her.

***

The white envelope in Mrs. Harding's hand created tension, even for herself. Her gaze flickered from one student to the other as she shoved up a bosom with one arm.

The examination results had come in for Annie Walsh School. Who passed the exam? More importantly, who does the school want?

The quiet was ominous. Even the car horns on Kissy Road had fallen silent.

"If you applied for Annie Walsh School, please stand up."

I had to lean on Joy to support my legs.

The usual rumors had begun to fly as soon as we handed in the application forms. Even more children than spaces in secondary schools this year. Stricter standards from the best schools. Moneyed families had bought the answers for their children. The machines broke down in Ghana. Exams would be canceled.

But the Common Entrance Examination sheets did come on time, from Ghana or wherever. My neighbors on Goree Street came out before the cars on exam day.

"Good luck!" Ma Abel made a fist.

Mammy Porter and Mammy Penina grinned from their window seals.

From his porch, Mr. Pinkney shouted, "Mameh, I know you're going to kill that exam."

At the bottom of Goree Street, the reserved Mrs. Kallay—who had never sat in a schoolroom—stood in her veranda to wish me good luck. I choked, thanking her.

A woman carrying her pepper to the market promised me that Allah will guide me through the exams. Of course, there were other students from my neighborhood taking the exam, but I must have been the first one on the street.

My cousin Baimba, keeping guard from the gate of his house on Magazine Cut, saw me before my blurred pupils could make him out.

"If that exam knows who its mother is, it better not give you a hard time."

I sucked in the tears running over my teeth. Baimba's tap on my shoulder energized my steps into the examination hall of Trinity School.

***

When Mrs. Harding was picking up the scattered books on my desk, telling me to, "Leave right away," and go tell my parents to "See somebody," I promised myself I would not cry.

My parents will certainly see somebody, and all will be well. I will go to Annie Walsh School, even if Mrs. Forster has not called me for an interview.

I had passed the exam, after all. If the *somebody* does not work, there is also Pa, who always makes sure my mother gets whatever she wants.

Standing in the empty schoolyard in front of the new Parsonage House, my mind rushed back to the days in Class Three, when I embarked on a fundraising campaign. I attended Thanksgiving service, against my parents' wish. I was dreaming of rising out of the trench in which I saw my mother, who never completed elementary school.

Without notice, my legs softened from under me. I was on the pebbled ground, head tucked between my legs. I didn't care how far my voice went, and I made no attempt to wipe my face.

My dream at five years old, when I first met the head teacher of Holy Trinity Infant School and told myself I would be like her, was now nothing more than over-ripe banana squashed under an army truck, with nothing left to scrape up and save.

***

"Your father will see someone," Attatie was wiping her face incessantly, with a cloth from the pocket of her sewing machine. "We'll give everything we have, and someone will talk to the principal. Misses Forster will accept you in her school."

"Everyone…" I cried. "Everyone is going to Annie Walsh **School, except me.**"

"Don't worry. You, too, will go to Annie Walsh School."

"All of my friends have been called in for interviews."

"We know how to wrangle in this country. You *will* go to Annie Walsh School." She wiped my face with my uniform skirt.

"We are Marabous, but we are good Marabous." She held up the uniform with both hands, moving it around to find a dry spot with which to wipe my face further. "My grandfather was a customs officer under the colonial government. My grandfather bought a tin house right here in Freetown, way back in colonial days."

My mother untied and retied her headscarf. She held me by the shoulder and pulled me into the house.

"We are not natives," she said.

Gone to Buy Salt

I was three years old when my little brother left, "to buy salt," my
mother said, dabbing her eyes with the edge of her cotton wrapper.
Mustapha could not yet even sit by himself, let alone walk.
*Why send him on the streets to buy salt? Why did you not send Miss Tor, or even
Mohammed, the eldest? Why not even me?*

I was Mustapha's armchair in the days before I started school. My
mother would sit me on the linoleum floor and put a ball of old clothes
between Mustapha's hip and my groin. Then she would fold my hands
on the baby's chest, like a parapet, to prevent him from falling on his
face. I had to sit like that each time my mother was to rush to the
kitchen to stir a pot of groundnut stew, blow fire under a pot, or put an
urgent stitch on a client's dress. She sometimes stayed away longer than
my patience could endure. I could not take the baby drooling on my
hands, and my mother would come running back at the sound of his
shrills, to pull his head off the linoleum. Other times, when the thud
of his head on the floor was not loud enough for my mother to hear,
I did what I had seen her often do: put my finger in his mouth so he
could suck on it and forget his pain.

Our backyard filled up early on the day of Mustapha's departure,
with women in tie-dye wrappers, cobalt-blue cow cornea, coffee-col-
ored leaves, horizontal and vertical shapes. They arrived before the
sun, one heavy footstep after the other. My sister and I ran from our
bedroom at the sound of their weeping. There were Granny and Papa's
sisters and cousins from Boyle Street, and Attatie's aunties and cousins
from Sackville Street. Our eager hugs quieted their sobs, and they held
us close to their chests.

"You must buck up." Aunty Mariama was holding a saucer with buttered bread. "Take a small bite."

Grandma Ndamba put down the fanner of rice and advised Aunty Mariama to give my mother a cup of hot cocoa instead. Aunty Fatmata pointed to a try with a cup of cocoa.

"The hot cocoa will clear the breeze from her stomach," she said.

My mother took a quick sip, then stuck the cup back in Aunty Mariama's hand.

Grandma Ndamba came forward. "Amie," she called in a gravelly voice. "Can you be upset with Allah?"

The women answered for her. "*Astahkfirullai*—may Allah himself forbid that thought."

"Can you fight Allah?"

The women chorused, "*Astahkfirullai.*"

Grandma pointed to Amie and me. "Will you leave your other children behind to go after Mustapha?"

"*Astahkfirullai.*"

Attatie release a deep sigh. Indeed, she looked as though she were ready to leave the rest of her children to go after the force that had snatched her youngest son.

"We cannot fight Allah's will," Aunty Fatmata said.

"*Walai*," the women chorused.

"You're still young," Granny said. "*Insh'Allah*, you will give my son another child, another son."

Papa's mother sat on the only high-chair in the yard and condensed her grief into the movement of her hands inside a calabash. She added water and sugar before rounding up the dough and tossing it inside a smaller calabash. It was not the first time she was preparing *fourah* for a grandchild. She put the calabash on the dirt floor and made no attempt to dust off her black velvet wrapper.

"Where are the kola nuts?" she said.

No one heard her. The choruses of *insh'Allahs*, and the advices on how best to get my mother to put something in her stomach, together with the pounding of pestles, had all muffled Granny's voice.

She asked again, without bothering to raise her voice. One of the younger women sitting on the bench next to her shouted that Aunty Mariama had the kola nuts.

"Not me!" Aunty Mariama shouted back. "Fatmata was getting them from Dove Cut."

Aunty Fatmata pointed the defeathered fowl toward a younger woman.

"Don't you remember," she said, "Marie Kissy was getting the kola nuts?"

"Me?" Marie Kissy gasped.

She was Papa's cousin. Dark and twiggy, she was nicknamed after the town where she lived.

"No one gave me money for kola nuts," she said. "No one told me to get kola nuts."

"Yes, someone did, Marie Kissy." The ropes bulged in Aunty Fatmata's throat. "I told you to come get the money early this morning and go to Dove Cut for kola nuts."

Marie Kissy grumbled about some in the family always casting her as the irresponsible one. About the times when others had made mistakes or did something wrong, and no two ears heard about it.

"All right," Granny said. "Don't pull yourself out of God's hand for something so small."

She untied the knot at the edge of her wrapper and pulled out a few coins.

Before Marie left to get the kola nuts, Aunty Fatmata insisted that she was irresponsible for her teenage years. Marie turned around with a knotted face, but before she could speak, everyone chorused for her to ignore Aunty Fatmata.

Aunty Mariama said, "She's not irresponsible. She's just getting too much of the breeze from the Kissy sanitarium."

Laughter flooded into the morning gloom. Even Attatie broke a smile.

When they returned to their tasks, the women's faces were less drawn, their voices lighter, until Miss Tor came to announce, "The men are back from the hospital," and folded her lips.

***

Attatie's grandmother had packed Miss Tor's suitcase, along with her wedding gifts. Both Attatie and Miss Tor were raised by Attatie's grandmother. So at ten years old, when Attatie got married, their grandmother sent her along to wash plates and fetch water until the bride's own children were old enough to help around the house.

Most of my pre-school trips outside the house were in Miss Tor's company. She came home from school, bathed me, rubbed burnt palm oil on my skin, and took me to Mammy Coker's tin store to buy ginger cake and peppermint sweets. She was the only older person who didn't remind me not to ask questions or to keep my mouth shut in the presence of adults.

"Why didn't Mother send you to buy salt?" I was sitting next to her, against the white wall that separated the dining area from the parlor.

"Do you know what they do to babies who leave before they can walk?" she replied.

When I shook my head, she put a finger on the bronze space between her ear and shoulder.

"They put a mark here, before taking them away."

"Why?"

"So they will not come back."

"Why shouldn't they come back?"

"You'll know when you grow up."

It was the first time I inhaled the perfume of lavender and cloves. It came from the parlor where the male members from Boyle Street and Sackville Street were seated in a large circle on reed mats. Most had their eyelids squeezed shut, Qur'ans in hand, their voices in unison. Some sat on their knees. Others stretched out their legs, their bodies swaying inside of the qur'anic verses they uttered.

Papa sat at the far end of the circle, closer to the front door.

A man with a white beard, much older than the rest, shouted, "Al-Fatiah!"

And Miss Tor stretched her hand out. "They're about to take him away," she whispered in my ear.

"Where are they taking him?" I whispered back.

"Shhh! They're taking him up the road, near Mammy Coker's store, where he can continue on his own."

"May he travel well," I heard one of the men say.

"May he return a good *malaika*, and shield us," another said.

"Ameena," they chorused.

One by one, they stood up and trudged outside. I could see Papa in full view now, sitting next to Uncle Sumaila. Mohammed sat next to him, his face in a crisp.

Then I saw it—a small wooden box the size of a gallon pan, in the same spot where I used to help Mustapha sit up straight.

"That's the car Mustapha will use to go on his errand," Miss Tor whispered in my ear.

My baby brother riding a gallon pan car, on an errand to by salt. The questions abounded, but I did not know how to put them into words.

When most of the men had left the room, Uncle Sumaila picked up the box and held it like a parcel, on his side. Then he laid it on the windowsill, and another man standing on the veranda received the parcel through the window.

The mats were still on the floor when I entered the empty room and sat on the spot where my baby brother's car had been. The smell of lavender and cloves was still thick in the hot air. For days, it was like an unwanted playmate that wouldn't let go of my dress or the strands of my braids.

***

"I will cut off your feet if you dare cross that fence again." My mother waved the knife close to my face before pointing it toward the rickety fence that separated our house from Ma Abel's.

Amie and I usually profited from its missing lower planks, to pass over into Ma Abel's yard and enjoy her rice bread and coconut cakes. There was also Emma and Josiah to play with. The games were sometimes challenging, like simply holding wood and axe from their backyard, or touching hot ambers of coal with our bare hands. Other times, it was admiring Mohammed and Josiah's ability to slingshot pigeons. When it was only Emma, Amie, and me, we played *akra* or hopscotch.

"Did you hear what I said?"

"Yes, Ma."

"I will cut off those lips, too, if I catch you eating anymore of Ma Abel's food."

"Yes, Ma."

I remained stooped on the floor in front of her, calm and focused on the splashing blood as she slammed one beef cube after another into a deep bowl. I could have asked questions: *What have I done? What has Ma Abel done? Did I eat her pork?* But I knew the rules.

"Emma and Josiah can come over here to play, if they want," my mother said. "But you or your sister can never again go over to their yard."

Who was it that said there's never a space too tight for a determined fowl to lay eggs? Only a few days after Attatie's edict, a scheme popped out of my five-year-old brain.

It was Ma Abel's Saturday evening ritual to come out of the backyard kitchen, holding hot rice bread crusts. "Mameh!" she would call, and I would abandon whatever I was doing to come running toward her yard.

My plan that Saturday, was to play as close as possible to the fence, to avoid Ma Abel having to shout out my name for Attatie to hear. Then I would get my share of rice bread crumps, eat it, and return inside without my mother noticing.

It worked. Ma Abel came out of her backyard kitchen, dragging an old pair of slippers and holding pieces of rice bread at her fingertips. Before she could open her mouth, my little hands were held out in front of her. I ate quickly, darting furtive looks behind me. The yard was empty except for the two of us—Ma Abel chewing on her gums and wiping her hand on a faded robe, and I chewing equally heavenly. I was well into my third or fourth bite when I heard my name.

"I'm here, Ma!"

I turned away from Ma Abel while trying to swallow with the speed of a hungry dog. Swiped my mouth with the back of my hand and moved toward the house.

"Here, where?"

My mother's ardent voice met me halfway between the backyard kitchen and the back door.

"Here at front of the door, Ma. I'm coming, Ma."

I reached the doorstep and could not bring myself to throw away the remaining delicacy in my hand. So I folded it inside my palm, believing that my mother would neither see nor smell the fresh-baked rice bread.

"Why did you take so long to answer?"

My mother was sitting on a chair next to the window. I stood as far away from her as I could manage.

"I was on my way coming, Ma. That's why."

"What have you been eating?"

To my five-year-old brain, the question came out of nowhere. What's more, is that it was followed by a yank that brought my mouth to my mother's face. And like a toothbrush, a finger scraped the inside of my mouth.

"What are you eating?" She held out bits of rice bread on her fingertip. "Who gave this to you?"

"Nothing, Ma. No one gave me anything, Ma."

"Where did you get this from?" She had wrestled out the piece I was hiding inside my palm.

Even if I had been older and quicker, with a brilliant excuse, there would have been no time to present it. The lightning appeared to have come first, my jaws under electrocution, before I heard the spank and its stinging impact.

"Did I not tell you not to eat anything from Ma Abel's house?

My face went numb after the second hit.

"Do you want to go away the way Mustapha did?"

"No, Ma," I murmured from deep inside my throat.

I did not try, or even want to understand the relationship between eating from Ma Abel's hands and going away like my baby brother. My focus was on avoiding the hits as I swirled like a bee tied to the axis of her hand.

"Papa!" I screamed.

"When Mustapha left, did you see him come back?" The hitting continued.

"No, Ma. Papa!" I knew he was in the house somewhere.

"Do you want to die?" She grabbed my lips and twisted them around. "Then why do you go over to Ma Abel's house?"

"Papa!" I called in a muffled voice.

"Why do you accept food from her? Are you hungry? Do we not give you food every day?"

"Yes, Ma. You give me food, Ma."

It was clear now that Papa's help was not coming, so I put more effort into wriggling out of her hand. It felt like I was harnessed to a vehicle. I twisted to one side, only to be pulled in harder on the other. I went lower on the linoleum, only to be dragged back up. But the exercise seemed to exhaust my mother, and the pounding stopped. And I promised, under duress, to never again eat Ma Abel's rice bread.

The Taste of Kola Nut Juice

About two years after Mustapha's passing, Granny arrived at the bottom of our veranda. She had a cotton head tie over her forehead and ears, and a velvet wrapper covered her enormous hips. The sun was not yet out, but she climbed only a few steps and wiped dripping sweat with the bottom of her half-gown. Every bit of flesh on her body was like meat on a rolling hanger, as she climbed the remaining five or six steps into our veranda.

Ma Abel saw or heard Granny, and stepped out onto her porch, wearing an old wool hat. I sensed trouble.

Would Granny raise her voice at Ma Abel and say, *How dare you send away my grandson to buy salt?* Would Ma Abel's mouth dilate, a finger to Granny's chest, while she said, *Me?*

Would Granny remove her head tie and hiss, *Yes, you?*

Even more dreadfully, would Granny pull me in front of her and say, *And you even gave my granddaughter rice bread, so she, too, would go and buy your salt?*

Then Ma Abel would look at me, and I would have to endure the smell of the mentholatum and burnt palm oil inside of Granny's legs, because I would not face Ma Abel and lie that I did not eat her rice bread.

But Granny and Ma Abel did not fight.

"Isn't it too early to be out, Amie, in this harmattan season?" Ma Abel said, as Granny panted on the veranda steps.

Ma Abel herself was wearing a heavy cardigan. Granny patted her velvet wrapper and said she was all right "but for these thighs," the flesh of which she squeezed.

"I tell you, Ma Abel, these thighs aren't mine."

Ma Abel, in turn, pressed on her hips which, she didn't think belonged to her.

The conversation ended with Ma Abel prescribing a mixture of burnt palm oil, sheer butter and *mentholatum* for Granny's thighs, and Granny recommending a wrap for Ma Abel's hips.

My mother had brought home a new baby on the eve of Granny's visit. It was a gift, I was told, from Dr. Smith. Mammy Porter and Mammy Penina waved vigorously from their windowsills when my mother stepped out of the taxicab, carrying the pink bundle. Families came from Sackville Street and Boyle Street to cry, "O ya, beautiful stranger! Fine pikin," and express hope that the stranger had come to stay.

The first person that came to visit the stranger was Ma Abel. To my surprise, Attatie did not stop her holding her new baby. She put the baby on one arm and caressed its curly, slick-black head.

"O ya, beautiful stranger! Fine pikin. Looking just like her late grandfather!"

Ma Abel then sealed her lips to the stranger's ear and told her she had "a handsome brother and two beautiful sisters," and "a grandmother next door who bakes delicious rice bread and coconut cake."

"No, no," Attatie said in a gentle tone. "This stranger is too young to eat rice bread and coconut cake."

Papa backed her up with a reminder that, in addition to Ma Abel, the stranger had a grandmother at Boyle Street would happily light up her coal pot.

Ma Abel swelled up. "Nonsense!" She whispered into the baby's ear again, "I, too, am your grandmother, you hear?"

Even before the baby came home from the hospital, everyone treated her as though she didn't have a name. Miss Tor was the only person I could talk to about it.

"I'll tell you after your bath tomorrow," she said, "if you don't cry."

There was not much hope there. Papa, for days in a row, said, "I'll tell you her name when I return from work."

After I gave Mohammed a portion of my cassava leaves rice, and did him all manner of errands, he admitted he didn't know the baby's name, and neither did Amie. So when the baby came home, I broke a house rule and followed every visitor into the parlor, hoping to hear one of them address the baby by her name, but no adult was careless enough to fall into my trap.

Then granny arrived on the veranda, early that morning, and trudged into the living room. The place had been transformed into a backyard, with a kitchen bench and paraphernalia of bottles and plastic bowls in the center of the room. They added to the library of questions I had stored up: *Why was Mustapha sent away to buy salt? Why did he go with a mark on his neck? Why is it wrong for me to eat Ma Abel's rice bread? Why does the new baby not have a name? Why the concern that she might not stay?*

Granny knew her place was in the kitchen bench, so she sat and tucked her wrapper between her legs, like a codpiece, leaving her excess thigh flesh to droop over the bench. Attatie handed her the baby in a pink blanket. From that moment on, every one of Granny's actions—from unfolding the baby out of the blanket, to the kola nut juice she spat in its mouth—was a ritual she began with, *"Bismilai rahagh mani Rahim."*

The baby looked like a single stick inside an empty matchbox, rolling from one end of Granny's enormous arm to the other.

"Bismilai rahagh mani Rahim. Oh, is this my beautiful stranger, my new cover, to keep me warm, to protect me from shame?"

The baby responded with serene composure, until the winds rushed in from the veranda.

"You chose to arrive at Harmattan season, did you not? What is the complaint about, my beautiful stranger?"

Attatie pulled the pink blanket over the baby's frame.

I was sitting on a thin wooden slab underneath the window through which Mustapha's coffin had traveled. It was usually my seat of choice when I was allowed in the room with adults.

"Will you help Granny bathe the baby?" Attatie said.

I rushed to stand by Granny's side. Miss Tor had not said the type of mark they put on Mustapha, but I was looking for any mark at all on this stranger's neck.

The baby was numb to the ritual bath going on around her. She seemed engaged, instead, in a silent battleground of gurgling and punching the air above her.

"Open your eyes," I said, feeling I could have my way with the little thing.

"A girl's eyes should not be open." Granny gathered some of the bathwater in a cupped fist, which she brought to the baby's mouth. *"Bismilai rahagh mani Rahim"*

She drank in quiet gulps.

"Why don't you have a name?" I said.

Granny replied that babies do not have names.

"But Mustapha had a name," I said to the baby. "His name was Mustapha."

"Pass the soap," Granny said.

The scour of a black soap and loofah gourd combination were part of the nightmare I associated with baths at that time. Was Granny going to wash the baby's body and face like Miss Tor washed mine? Was she going to let soap get into her eyes?

It was not long before I had an answer worse than I could have imagined.

"Pass the soap," Attatie repeated.

My fingers went right through the sticky ball and came out covered in nasty black goo. I ducked them into the bathwater, making splashes that wet the floor and Granny's legs. She gripped my hand and sent it flying out of the bowl.

"We're not a people who smell," she said, justifying the black foam that now covered the baby's teeny frame, even as it shrieked for passers on Goree Street to hear.

Granny pressed on, passing the gourd inside the folds of the baby's thighs, catching a limb as it attempted to fly, working on the spaces between the toes, between the fingers, the armpits, the wrinkles in the neck space.

"You must not carry around the stench you came with," was Granny's response to the shrieks.

The only part of the baby's body spared was the navel, covered with a now-soiled white bandage.

When Granny was done with the soaping, the baby looked like a log in a firepit after the pot had been taken off the firestones, and before the winds come through to blow away the ash.

"You'll thank your granny someday, when you can sit among your peers and not have to worry about body odor.".

Attatie thanked Granny. I was imagining a noisy, stinky baby world.

"*Bismilai rahagh mani Rahim.* "

When Granny finally immersed her into the bowl of water, the little one made soft, tiresome grunts. My mother held out a small white towel. The baby's sounds grew more tiresome, weaker, like someone saying thank you on her last breath. I thought she would not cry anymore.

"Get the shea butter," Attatie said.

I took my time uncovering the first two jars before picking up the shea butter from the third one.

"*Bismilai rahagh mani Rahim.* This will protect you from the cold you've been complaining about," Granny said to the limp body on her lap.

She picked up the cloth ball and began massaging it like a stress ball. My mother picked up a plate with a large rock and went out through the back door.

"Look at her," granny called to me. "Isn't your sister beautiful?"

To me, it looked like a cockroach had just jumped out of a bottle of palm oil, onto Granny's lap.

Attatie stayed outside for a while, before returning with the pebble, gray smoke oozing from its pores. She placed it on the linoleum next to granny's bench. With one hand over the baby's torso, Granny bent over to make quick dabs of the cloth ball on the smoking stone. The cloth took on smoke. Then she untied the soiled white bandage around the baby's navel, and to my horror, dabbed the hot ball onto the navel.

"*Alhamdulilai!* We have good lungs!"

It was as if the house would collapse under the vim of the baby's backlash. Granny was unperturbed. She continued with one or two more dabs, from the pebble to the navel, before finally wrapping up the navel in a new bandage and moving on to the makeup stage.

With tiptoe care, she intercepted the baby's punches to apply a teal eyeliner on its bottom eyelid. It was something I remember always dreading, when Attatie used the eyeliner on me, afraid the spiky tip of the gold vial was reaching for my pupils.

"Get your grandmother the kola nut." Attatie cut through my distraction.

Granny took a bite of the kola nut, chewed it for several minutes, then between her thumb and index finger, brought out a crushed slush that she held over the baby's mouth.

"You're giving the baby your spittle!" I shouted. "That's dirty."

I was, at that age, always within reach of my mother's cane, but it was Granny who reacted.

"I'm going to tell you something today." Her voice was the high pitch she would use with an undesirable neighbor, or someone she referred as, *those people*—someone, she would say, who had never had kola nut spat into their mouths.

"I don't care if you're a day old, a year old, or if you're seventy years old, you must always remember what I'm going to tell you today." The wall on her face was erect.

Granny never used the cane or laid a hand on me, nor on Mohammed or Amie. She never even once raised her voice on any of us. Had I pushed her too far? Will she be like Attatie, and slap or whip me?

"It doesn't matter where you go," Granny said, "it doesn't matter what you become…you must remember who *we* are."

My siblings and I, we were Granny's velvet wrapper. We kept her warm. We made up for all she gave up to raise her children after her husband died—when Papa, the oldest, was only seven years old. She had refused to remarry. She had preferred to rely on her *agidie* business because, she said, she didn't want to share her children with a man who was not their father.

"For those things your eyes will witness and want to talk about," she continued, "for those things your ears will hear and want to repeat, be it in the parlor, in the bedroom, or on the streets…"

My mother's face had assumed the same look she wore on the day Mustapha was taken away.

"I want to show you today, what happens when you do not stop and think—think before you talk. Think before you act. So I'm putting this kola nut in your mouth today, so that even at this tender age, you will experience the bitterness that will befall you, if you do not learn to know when to talk and when to keep quiet."

Granny was addressing the baby, who like me, reacted strongly to the bitter taste on its tongue, as Granny named those things *we* Mandinga people do not do; *we do not drink alcohol, we do not eat pork, we do not marry strangers, we do not push ourselves forward.*

The Woman in Paw-Paw Skin

My mother found me on the veranda, trying to make myself disappear under the scrutiny of the Fernando Po woman. She always pressed her silky hair backward and wore dresses that exposed her pawpaw skin. All day long, she sat on Ma Abel's porch to stare at me through rusty, zinc eyes. She seldom spoke, and except for Ma Abel, I noticed few people around her. When she did speak, she sounded like she was inside the transistor radio. When she addressed me, I could only pick up words like, *Go to school,* and, *How much years,* or, *How you do.* Usually after I had been buttonholed in front of her long enough to defrost. She would repeat her questions several times while I bowed my head in response.

Attatie saw her talking to me once and immediately pulled my arm into a twist behind my back and hurled my body inside the house. I don't think I cried. I wasn't comfortable with the woman, anyway. A few days after, Papa, Attatie, and Aunty Olay were sitting on the veranda.

"My house is finally free of witches," Papa said triumphantly.

I was in my usual seat—the slab below the window where Mustapha's coffin had traveled.

"*Subhuanalai!*" Aunty Olay threw her stout hands over her head.

"That's right," Papa said, and went on to explain how he had watched the witch, "just the other day, walking into my yard the way she usually does, through the broken fence the children used to get to Ma Abel's yard."

Should I run and tell Mohammed and Amie about the witch, or should I stay and listen more?

Leaving would have exposed my crime of eavesdropping on adult conversation.

"Except, this time, she stopped right there." Papa was pointing to a spot I could not see from where I sat. "She didn't know what made her stop." His said.

"Imagine what would have happened had we not wised up in time?" Attatie said.

Aunty Olay shouted, *"Lailahailallaw muhammadurasululah!* You would've lost all of your children. She would have eaten them all up, from Mohammed to Amie to Mameh, one after the other."

Imagine my regret, eavesdropping on adult conversation! For days, I was convinced a loose witch was laying on the bed I shared with my sister. Mohammed confirmed my fears when he said he himself had more than once seen the witch of whom Papa spoke, and Amie was equally ghost stricken. I insisted on sleeping in my parents' bed without daring to give them an explanation, or associate any of our neighbors with sending my baby brother on an errand to buy salt.

***

Ma Abel had buttonholed a woman to explain the story of the Christian woman Papa's grandfather had married. Marie Kissy and Josiah's mother were preparing takeaway bags with bread, banana, orange, and *fourah* balls. Miss Tor settled me in a corner of the bedroom to oil my body and dress me up.

"Would you brighten my day with a good morning?" Josiah's mother cajoled me.

After I brightened her day, she told me I was soon going to know my baby sister's name.

Earlier that morning, Miss Tor had walked me naked past a bleating sheep, toward the wash yard. Aunty Mariama put down her sieve and pulled on the hairless mound of my groin. Aunty Fatmata took a break from pounding rice to slap my behind.

"Leave my granddaughter alone," Granny joked, pressing rice flour into tiny balls.

Steam was flowing out of a three-legged cauldron on a fireplace set outside the kitchen. Marie Kissy and my other older cousins arrived carrying large wicker baskets filled with bread loaves. Grandma Ndamba was counting kola nuts in fig leaves.

The men were in the parlor, sitting in a circle the way they did for Mustapha's funeral. In the center, where Mustapha's box had been, was a large tray with scores of kola nuts on top of a large mound of *fourah*. As more men arrived and the room filled up, I wriggled my way through the men to talk to Uncle Sumaila. He rubbed my head, joked that I was the only woman not helping with the food preparations, and gave me a penny.

The crowd of men thickened, and my mother came out of her bedroom, flanked by Aunty Olay and a few other friends. Aunty Olay held the baby, its head wrapped in one of Attatie's head ties. She handed it over to Uncle Sumaila, and the women returned to the bedroom. The men went into their trances, reading verses from the Qur'an, and ended with the *Al-Fatiah* prayer.

Someone shouted for Mariama Conteh to hurry up with the cups. Granny used an enormous gourd spoon to pour rice porridge into a bucket. Aunty Mariama brought the bucket and cups into the house and handed it over to one of the men. Aunty Fatmata brought the men wicker baskets of bread and fruits, and a man came in with a basket full of pieces of raw mutton. The men took care of their own service. The women did the same in the backyard.

Finally, the crowd depleted. I was leaning against Granny's lap, my head buried in a cup of rice porridge when she poked me on the shoulder.

"Your sister's name is Fatmata. Like Aunty Fatmata."

I raised my head from the porridge cup to absorb the information. The first thing I saw was a set of eyes different from those of the women in my yard. The Fernando Po woman had come to sit on Ma Abel's back porch. Miss Tor had told me she was the witch who had sent Mustapha on the salt errand because she didn't have children of her own. But maybe because I was leaning on the comfort of granny's thighs, I did not avoid her eyes.

Qur'anic School

"We're going to learn to read the Qur'an!" Alpha Ghazali swung his arms around a wiry waist. "Are you ready?"

"Yeeees!" I joined the chorus of scarved five- to eight-year-old's bouncing against each other on the reed mat.

Scarves slipped down our shoulders, *fourah* balls rolled out of their walnut tablets. They followed the red and white kola nuts that had made their way onto the dusty cement floor of the Islamia classroom. We lost some of the pennies we had collected so far, going after the fleeing fourah and kola nuts. Fathers, uncles, older brothers crept onto the floor to join the recovery effort and wipe our tears.

Alpha Ghazali ignored it all and plied himself into two in front of us.

"But, oh," he clasped his hands and bounced in tune with our restless selves, "the Arabic answer is *naa'mu.*"

The word amused us.

"*Naa'mu, naa'mu, naa'mu.*" We wiggled and wagged our heads. "*Naa'mu, naa'mu, naa'mu.*"

It became a high-pitch song. Again, our sequined scarves slipped down our shoulders, *fourahs* and kola nuts rolled off our tablets. And again, the adults rushed to our rescue.

Learning to read the Qur'an was one of those things Granny said we Mandingas did, after the bathing and the naming ceremony. Papa pinched a piece off my *fourah* and placed the first penny on my tablet. My uncles and Mohammed followed. And later, when we got home, Attatie pinched off half the *fourah* before we set off for Granny's house.

On the way, Mohammed convinced me that my pennies were safer in his pocket. Granny hugged me and the tablet all at once, took several pinches off the *fourah*, bit off some of the kola nut, and put several pennies on the tablet. She called her tenants to come and do the same. Then she named all the houses on Boyle Street to which Mohammed should take me so that extended family members and her friends could share in my indoctrination into Islamic school.

With my pennies bulking Mohammed's pockets, we stopped at only one or two houses, and one of them was because the old lady called out to us before we even saw her sitting in front of her gate. Then we rushed to the Fullah sweet shop on Bombay Street, and bought toffee, biscuits, and Diamints. And every Sunday morning after that, I followed Mohammed and Amie to Islamic lessons at the Mandinga Mosque.

***

Papa told me to sit on the slab at the bottom of Granny's house and listen to the teachers at Ahmaddiya School.

"That way, you would've gone to school."

It made sense. I was not yet five. An old apple tree was the only thing that separated the school's two-story zinc structure from Granny's yard. Besides, the school's large casement windows were always wide open, and the teachers spoke loudly.

Papa bought me a schoolbag like the one Amie had. Attatie put my lunch of bread and jam in it. And Miss Tor walked me every morning before she went to school, to the junction of Goree Street and Bombay Street, where she looked for an adult to hold my hand and deliver me to Granny's gate.

Granny's house was a daycare center for her pre-school grandchildren and others in the neighborhood. I played with the other children only until the Ahmadiyya school bell rang, when I then would refuse the most beseeching offer to play. Instead, I sat on the cement slab and perked my head up, moving it from one classroom window to the other. That is how I learned to sing the "ABC Song" and "Baa, Baa, Black Sheep." From there, I practiced the Arabic alphabet.

When the schoolchildren came out to play, I went and stood on the other side of the apple tree. When the girls skipped rope, I welcomed the red dirt on my face and waited for them to ask me to join them. On one of their morning breaks, a group of girls stood in a circle playing *akra*. It was an arid day, and the red dust was exceptionally powdery. The leader of the group stood in the center of the circle, clapped her hands, jumped and thrust her right foot forward. The first player also clapped and jumped at the same time as the leader, and put her left foot forward. She had lost. She shuffled back to her place in the circle, and the girls giggled after her.

The leader moved to the next player, clapped, jumped and put her left foot forward. The second player had put her right foot forward. She lost, and the girls emitted another loud chortle. The third and fourth player also lost. I was certain I could win where the other girls had lost.

The entire playground looked as if a bomb had just gone off in the schoolyard. Dust covered their naked feet, and their white blouses were now cocoa brown.

"I can do it!" I shouted.

Every one of the girls turned around. Every face held the most vicious scorn little girls could muster. But it was my cousins who laughed first. They tumbled over each other on the dirt ground. Then the girls released fits of laughter. I backed away slowly, my teary eyes still on the schoolyard.

It was probably a few weeks or months later, when I was still not yet five years old, that Attatie sewed me an Ahmadiyya School uniform. Turned out, she had a friend who taught at the school. Then one morning, dressed in a royal blue tunic and white buttoned blouse, I climbed the school steps, in the hands of Mariama Conteh. The class was already in progress, with everyone doing different things. I recognized one or two of the akra-playing girls that had rejected me, and followed Mariama Conteh past their classroom and up a creaking wooden staircase into an upstairs room, where she introduced me to a small, light-skinned woman in a silk head tie.

"This is your teacher," she said. Her name is Aunty Jallie."

I had never seen her before, but she looked like what I wanted my teacher to be. I fell in love with her, even before she smiled and took my hand and told the students to meet their new friend. From where I stood in the classroom, I could see the casement windows, but Granny's window appeared to have disappeared below it. I sat at an empty desk next to the teacher.

During break, my classmates—Class Two girls—circled around me to play *akra*. My cousins watched me from Granny's yard and could not laugh.

The Big School

My mother held my hand on the gravel of Holy Trinity Infant School. I could see neither the ground, nor where the dark-blue pole the other parents were holding onto went. An adult voice was calling out names: Christiana Johnson, Thomas Cole, Rexford Jarett, Gabriel Johnson, Frederick Smith, Douglas Carew. Parents answered and squeezed their way forward, pulling a uniformed child behind them, before disappearing inside the thick crowd in front of me.

"You know who that woman is that is calling the names," my mother bent down to whisper in my ear.

I shook my head, too nervous to speak.

"That's Mrs. Jarrett," she said.

I didn't know who Mrs. Jarrett was. I only knew I was at the school where Amie and Mohammed went. The big school.

Attatie said Mrs. Jarrett was the big teacher of the big school.

Mrs. Jarrett called out more names. parents came forward, tugging their children behind them. The sun sparkled through newly opened spots, and I began to notice other poles and parts of a pastel-green building. Some five-year-olds were playing around some of the poles. Some simply rubbed their hands on it as if to help them stay calm. While others, like me, stared blankly into the vivid yellow and white checks of each other's uniforms.

Suddenly, most of the crowd was gone. I became nervous. What if Mrs. Jarrett doesn't call my name? What if the big school was nothing more than Attatie's promise to buy me a doll, or Papa's earlier promises to take me to the big school which always ended in him holding my hand and walking me up and down Goree Street, stopping for a distracting toffee at the Fullah sweet shop, and then back home. What if I had to continue at Ahmadiyya School?

Attatie had said our neighbors, Mammy Penina and Mammy Porter, had attended Trinity School. Mohammed said teachers at Ahmadiyya School didn't know how to speak English. He said the children there were mostly country people.

"The only thing they know is how to read the Qur'an," he said.

"Memuna Sillah."

"Present!" I shouted, exactly the way Mohammed had told me to.

The adults chuckled and commented on my urgency to start school.

Indeed, I remember pulling my mother after me, until I found myself on a smooth cement landing in front of a woman in gold-rimmed spectacles. Her uncovered hair was neatly groomed, and her dress patterned with large hibiscus on a solid white background. In front of her desk, I saw the ground where the marine-colored poles began. It was held erect by the cement landing on the corridor in front of the building. The pole didn't end in mid-air as I had initially thought while standing behind adults on the gravel. It continued up to a second-floor corridor, together with several others of its kind, like sentinels, upholding the pillars of education.

"Are you Memuna Sillah?" Mrs. Jarrett said, in a crisp, clear voice.

"Yes," I said, my own voice quivering.

Our gazes met and she squeezed her eyebrows together, as though to observe me with minute precision. I kept my focus locked on the spaces between the hibiscus on her dress. Then her eyebrows relaxed, her lips widened so I could see her teeth, like neat rows of peppermint candy. I didn't move a speck of my body. I didn't want to. I could smell her breath, the rose in her perfume. Her pawpaw skin and cowrie-shell eyes reminded me of the Fernando Po woman.

For a long time after that meeting, whenever I spoke with my parents about my future, when I spoke with Granny, or with my other relatives from Boyle Street or Sackville Street, I mentioned Mrs. Jarrett. I was going to grow up and become like her.

***

Mrs. Cole-Jones seated me amongst four boys at a round wooden desk: Mrs. Jarrett's son, Rexford; a thin-lipped boy called Frederick; boxy

Gabriel; and the mean Douglas, who always started the car racing game that unnerved me. They would kick their legs so vigorously under the table that I would have to hold my elbows above the desk to stop it from vibrating. I never complained to the teacher. It was my second year at Trinity School, and I still looked upon my teachers with awe. With their bare heads and short dresses, and the English they spoke, the teachers were a foreign species to me, like the Fernando Po woman.

I used to imagine Mrs. Cole-Jones in a wrapper and head tie, like the women in my family. Sometimes she wrapped her head in a taut knot—the style Granny said sent the message that you were a serious woman who had lost her husband. Other times, I gave her the style Granny said unmarried women wore, with most of her hair outside the head tie, and a loose knot with long, thin straps that flapped against her back as she walked.

Once, when Mrs. Jarrett read from the Bible during morning assembly, I slipped a cap-like head tie on her. It was those worn by married women with young children. It had a short knot tied, not too taut, at the back of her head, and it sat atop her head so that you had to tiptoe to see it. Once, against Amie's cries of liar, I swore Mrs. Jarrett wore head ties like my mother's.

Miss Jackson Doesn't Like You

Mary Bull was short and bulky, with short hair like a boy. I sometimes thought Miss Jackson intentionally sat her right behind me in class so she could make demands on me. If I refused her my pen, paper, or book, I got the usual, "You're ugly" curse. Sometimes she scribbled on the shoulder of my uniform with the tip of her fountain pen and made sure the ink dripped down my back. When Attatie would roar, "Did you not report this girl to the teacher," I would lie that she did it by mistake.

Mary became sour the day I dumped my newspaper-wrapped jam sandwich from home and went with the more popular fly-infested street food. It was on Barbara's orders. Barbara could buy any girl a loaf of bread with as many bean cakes as she liked. She pointed at Fredericka, Joy, and me, and ordered everyone else, including Mary, to clear out. Barbara was the parson's granddaughter, after all, and I associated her grandfather with endless amounts of money. I didn't believe she stole money.

Barbara sometimes took us on tours to the schoolyard parsonage. We observed Parson Samuel's image on the wall—a full head of parted hair, and a face like that of a contrite child. We tried his bed. We sat on his chair and drank water from his cups. By the time we left, our fingerprints covered the pages of his Bible.

Other tours took us to Fredericka's house next door, into her mother's bedroom, to the dining table that said everyone had rushed out of the house after breakfast, then to the spot where her elder sister and boyfriend kissed the other night, and ended with a loud goodbye to grandma, who, affixed on the windowsill, never seemed to notice us.

Joy introduced us to all the curse words we needed to survive Class Four. There was hardly a fight between her parents or neighbors that she didn't demonstrate for us in class. She hurled her sandals at the classroom wall, citing somebody's backside; she clenched her teeth and pointed a finger at someone's face; she lifted her uniform, pulled down her panties and exposed her naked behind. As her feigned anger grew, we learned new curse words, and her books, pencils and pens all went the way of her sandals, until the entire contents of her saddlebag were lying on the floor.

Backyard sweats and offerings were mainstays in my house. Shall I talk about them? Shall I take my friends home to see where the animal was slaughtered? Show them where my mother kept the bundle of grains tied inside the red and white cloth? Shall I take them inside my parents' bedroom, close the door and point them to the folded piece of paper hanging on a white thread behind the door plank?

"You see, that's Arabic written all over it."

I was around eight years old, and I knew that my homelife was different from that of my Trinity School friends. There was also the kola nut juice, maybe? Looking back now, I believe the overwhelming reason was Miss Jackson.

Miss Jackson wore her hair in a beehive which made her look taller than she really was. On top of that, she walked with her head up and patted her hair incessantly. I kept my distance from my teachers, but Miss Jackson kept her distance from me.

But there were girls in the classroom that brought Miss Jackson joy. She made passionate inquiries after the health of Barbara and Fredericka's parents. She bugged those girls who did not give her the pleasure of their presence in church this or that Sunday.

Alas, my nemesis, Mary, noticed everything. When I failed to share anything with her, she whispered things in my ear that made me uncomfortable.

"Miss Jackson doesn't like you."

***

At Holy Trinity School, it didn't matter whether you read the Qur'an at home, or if your parents taught you how to address the wood figure under your pillow, you were expected to read the Bible and sing hymns at morning assembly.

Miss Jackson called the hymn one morning. I had mastered some of the tunes by now. I used to sing along with the Sunday morning church service on the radio as I swept the living room floor. I had memorized the Lord's Prayer and the twenty-third Psalm. I knew the line, *Lord hear our prayer,* should be followed by, *and let our cry come onto thee.*

"Go to hymn number one-ninety-three," Miss Jackson said.

We stood one behind the other, by class and by height, in front of the school's L-shaped building. The sun was young, but it brightened the banana-yellow of our plaid uniform. Our mood, too, was blitheful. Waves of bellicose breeze flew over from Dove Cut. They bumped up our skins and left orchid sepals stuck to our greasy braids. The tugging and pulling stopped only with the arrival of teachers on the corridor, each carrying a cane, a Bible, and a hymn book.

The teachers always led the tune for the hymns. The girls who went to church every Sunday joined in the second line, followed by the infrequent churchgoers, and lastly, girls like me who did not know the correct door through which one entered a church.

I flicked through the pages of my hymnal. Number 193, "O Jesus, We Adore Thee." I didn't remember ever singing that hymn at morning assembly, and I was a girl who never missed school.

The teachers led the tune. I felt safe joining in the third line. I got the melody and it seemed to work out. I did go off tune at the beginning of the fourth line, where I shortened the long note that started the line. In fact, a few of my fellow churchuntaughts also went off note, but we soldiered on, willing lackeys. *This is a hymn I could learn,* I thought.

We hit the fifth line. I tried to compensate for my error in the fourth line by singing a long note at the beginning. I did not anticipate change—the high pitch. Even the churchgoers seemed to struggle with it. The rest of us fell off the precipice, face down.

"Stop! Stop! Stop!" The headmistress came running down the corridor, breeze ballooning her wide frock. "That is not the way Christians sing!"

The teachers pointed their canes at us and shouted for the benefit of the headmistress.

"Who spoiled the hymn?" and, "Why can't you sing like Christians?" and, "This is bad, bad, bad!"

The headmistress arranged the belt around her waist and walked to the edge of the corridor.

"Now, sing after me."

She shaped two Os—one with her thumb and index finger, another with her mouth. Then she raised the hand with the cane and flexed her body forward, as though about to fly off the corridor ledge. The singing took off from there, with Mrs. Kissling drawing large circles in the air with her cane and singing loud enough to mask all our off-tunes.

***

We were not fully settled in class when Miss Jackson said, "How many Christians do we have in this class?" Worms had formed on her forehead.

I felt the tip of Mary's pen on my back.

"This is a Christian School." Miss Jackson appeared at her wit's end.

She counted an overwhelming number of Christian hands, but still despaired. Then she held her cane up, as though trying to touch the ceiling with it, and moved toward my desk. Mary's breath wetted my ears. I could hear timid groans from Mafula and the others.

Is Miss Jackson going to cane us because we were not Christians?

I did not moan or join the crying that had started at the back of the room. *That will give Mary too much to be happy about.* Besides, I was ready to repeat Ma Abel's line to Miss Jackson. *My grandfather had married a Christian woman.* I was going to tell her about my neighbors, Mr. Pinkney, Mammy Portor, Mammy Pennina, all of whom went to church on Sundays.

"I do not know," Miss Jackson tucked the cane inside of her dress to scratch her back—something she often did, "why we have so many native children in this school?"

I resented being called *native*. My mother resented being called *native*. It meant we were country people. *Native* meant my parents most likely were hawkers and market women, or maids and houseboys. *Native* meant my parents were not born in the city, and probably, neither was I. Of all the things Miss Jackson could do to me, she could *not* call me *native*.

But the teacher was already pacifying herself. She called the names of girls she saw in church on Sundays, followed by a deep sigh. Then she called out those she reminded were Christians, even if they didn't do their duty and make it to church—to Trinity Church—on Sundays. Girls like Mary and some of the Christian Yoruba girls in the class.

"Thank you, Jesus." Her eyeballs rolled around and rested on her Bible.

The class fed off the relief on her face. Everyone giggled. I giggled, too, happy to forget that Miss Jackson had called me a native.

"Miss Jackson doesn't like you."

A large blot stamped my exercise book. The tears came without warning. I was powerless to stop the first set of sobs.

"What's the matter with you now?" Miss Jackson sneered, her voice telling me I was wasting the time she was taking to ask the question.

With a decisive tug, I brushed off the tears with the back of my hand.

"Nothing," I replied, and picked up my fountain pen.

I thrusted it inside the dry inkwell, but it did not break.

***

On the day that Mafula gave Mary Bull the invitation to a fight, I was certain I'd soon see the last of Mary. Mafula was a hulk in an elementary school uniform. She spoke fast and with force. Everything about her was unkept—her hair, her uniform, her saddlebag. Miss Jackson often said she would be more useful helping her mother sell pepper and tomatoes at the market than coming to school.

It was often rumored that our headmistress, who had no child of her own, once offered to adopt Mafula's older and calmer sister—a clever girl—but their parents offered Mafula instead, which Mrs. Kissling summarily rejected.

The fight had its origins in the classroom.

Miss Jackson stood by Mafula's desk and fingered the rumpled edges of her exercise book

"Germs."

In the erupting laughter, Mary, sitting diagonally from Mafula, had the nerve to turn and laugh in Mafula's face.

As soon as Miss Jackson uttered, "Break time," Mafula turned to Mary and said, "Meet me behind the latrine.

I ate lunch in a hurry and summoned as many people as I could to the back of the latrine. The building was a rectangular block with four stalls papered with more obscene language than you would hear from the mouths of the boys at Dove Cut Wharf. The ring was a cemented space in the middle of a natural habitat at the back of the building. Mafula was already inside of it, waving her giant arms here and there.

"Where's the dog child?" she said.

No one answered.

She pointed to God above. "If I don't beat that bastard child to death today, I am not my mother's daughter."

"Yeh, yeh, give her a good beating!" No one dared not be on Mafula's side.

Then she spat and swore again that if Mary did not arrive before her spittle dried out, she would go drag her out of the classroom in the presence of Miss Jackson.

"Yeh, yeh, go drag her out! She's afraid of you."

Mafula's spittle was about to dry, and Mary still had not shown up.

"I want to piss." Mafula stalked toward the front of the latrine.

Of course, all thirty or so of us wanted to piss, too. By the time half of us were done pissing, the end-of-lunch bell was ringing.

Mary's head remained bowed on her desk the rest of the afternoon. She left in a hurry after school and did not come to school the next day or two. It wasn't unusual; Mary was one of those girls who came to school only when they were not needed for work at home.

By the time she returned to school, the scatter-brained Mafula had forgotten about the fight, leaving Mary free to resume her attacks on me.

I Could Make My Way to Church

It was evening in our house, so I had to step over drafting papers and geometry tools to tell Papa about the Thanksgiving service.

"Have you ever seen me go to church on Sunday?" He could have been addressing the keys on his calculator.

"Papa, my teacher said you should take me to church."

"Have you ever seen your mother go to church?"

"But Papa—"

"Have you ever seen Granny go to—"

"Papa, I want to go to church!"

He added more numbers to an arrangement of figures on a draft sheet, before continuing.

"Then go and talk to your mother." His focus remained on his work, fingers moving between the pens and pencils, rulers and triangles scattered over mounds of drafting papers on the floor.

"Attatie will tell me to come and ask you." I knew their game by now.

"Then go and tell her, and let her tell you to come and ask me."

My mother was sewing on the veranda.

"Tell your teacher to come and make me go to church." She put pressure on the machine's motor.

I was undeterred. Holy Trinity Church had decided the one-level wood building where Barbara's grandfather lived had to be expanded.

"It doesn't matter if you're Christian, Muslim, or pagan," Miss Jackson had said, "it is your duty to help build the new parsonage."

For weeks, the student population of Holy Trinity School delivered pennies and pounds in little brown envelopes.

"If you don't have money in those envelopes, don't bother come to school tomorrow."

That was Miss Jackson's daily mantra.

Some girls still had the guts to return their envelopes empty. Others, like Mary, stayed away for several days in a row. I guarded mine like my newborn. For days, I washed dirty plates, buttonholed uncles and aunts, fetched Papa's slippers, and in the end, my envelope felt like a thief's purse when I handed it to Miss Jackson.

I kneeled next to her sewing machine and reminded my mother of my efforts to fill those envelopes. I told her my Christian friends will be at the service.

"But can you sing church songs?"

She had heard me singing with the radio several times, but I fetched my hymnal, stood in front of her and sang hymns such as, "O Come All Ye Faithful" and "All Things Bright and Beautiful."

When she asked if I could read their Bible, I read parts of Genesis.

"Who's going to take you to the church that early in the morning?"

"It's like going to school," I said.

"But it's early, and there's no one on the streets that early on Sunday mornings."

"I can walk with Mister Pinkney," I said. "Or with Miss Fenella." They all go to Trinity Church."

"Then go and talk with your father first."

I waited for the right moment to return to Papa. It came after he had left with Uncle Sumaila for a meeting at the Mandinga Mosque. A client called to our house and left me with the usual long message. My siblings and I usually listened to Papa's clients with grave respect, then forgot everything they said as soon as we saw their backs. That morning, though, as soon as the client left, I tore off a piece of paper from my exercise book and wrote a letter to Papa in which I included the client's full name, address, phone number, and the address of the plot of land he had inquired about.

Look at this." Papa showed the letter to Uncle Sumaila when they returned. "She writes perfect English."

Uncle Sumaila read the letter. "Correct spelling and correct grammar."

They both agreed that I will end up going to England.

After Papa said, "From now on, every client's message should be written down," I made my move.

Papa's major worry was me leaving home early in the morning, all on my own. With peacock confidence, I convinced him and Uncle Sumaila that I could do it alone. I could arrive to church safely and get back home.

***

I went to the Thanksgiving service and vomited in the church.

"You won't go anywhere if you don't eat." Attatie followed me out of their bedroom.

"I'm not hungry," I said.

"Then take off that uniform and go back to bed." Attatie was already exchanging my beret and hymnal for the bread basket on the refrigerator roof.

She slammed a cup of cocoa on the table and adjusted the wrapper over her thin nightdress.

"Don't you know," she said, "that Christians go to church on a full stomach? It helps them sing better."

I wished there was anything other than sardines in the bread.

"That's enough of the cocoa," she said, beginning her usual choreography as I ate.

I folded a pinch of sardine inside of two small pieces of bread and stuck it down my throat.

"Don't swallow so fast," she snapped. "Chew that piece a bit longer."

I chewed the next piece a bit longer, then gulped it down with the cocoa.

"Finished." I put down the empty teacup and got up to negotiate the narrow space between her chair and mine.

As I waited for my beret and hymnal, Miss Jackson's words returned to me. *"Do not enter the church without it."* The new collection envelope she had given me was still between the pages of my hymnal.

"Go ask your father." Attatie swiped her palms down the thighs of her wrapper to indicate that she had no money.

Cowrie shells jingled behind the bedroom door.

"You should have asked for the money yesterday." Pa pulled the sheets over his head.

I punched his torso, which made him sit up.

"Whose child are you, anyway?" He pushed me away from his prayer rug and folded it.

"How much are you giving me?" I said.

He reached for his trousers on the wall hanger in front of him, then placed two pieces in my hand.

"Two shillings will not be enough to build the parsonage."

"Go ask your mother for the rest." He was already returning the sheets over his head.

I put the two shillings in my envelope and approached my mother. Before I could begin my appeal, she grabbed the envelope, licked and sealed it, then tucked it in my breast pocket.

"Tell your teacher this is all we have."

"But Miss Jackson said we should put more than two shillings in the envelope."

I don't think I knew how much I wanted. I just wanted a heavier envelope. The more money I could contribute towards the parsonage, the more attention I would get from my teacher.

"Then ask your teacher to give you the rest." Attatie was wiping crumbs off the dining table.

"Everybody in the class will take more money than me." I was fighting back a sob now.

"What about all the money you collected already?"

"Teacher said it is our responsibility to help build the parsonage."

"Then give her what your father put in the envelope."

"But the envelope has your name on it," I lied, knowing she could not read.

She halted between the dining chairs and the fridge.

"What's wrong with your teacher?" she shouted.

I braced my breast pocket. She could snatch the envelope and take it to Papa to read. I could end up not going to the service at all.

"Miss Jackson said, if we don't take money for the parsonage, we shouldn't bother go to school on Monday."

"Take off that uniform right now and get ready for Islamic School."

I snatched my beret and hymnal from her and didn't stop to find out if she really meant it.

★★★

Goree Street was as deserted as my parents feared, but not for long. I had barely completed the length of our fence when a mother appeared behind me, in pink ensemble and matching hat. Her husband was in black suit and rope-like tie, with two girls in Trinity School uniform. By the end of Goree Street, others had joined us: groups of older boys in dark suits, more Trinity school girls, women in bold yellows and blues and reds, with matching fanner hats and high heels. I moused my way behind them and cowered when an adult turned around to look at me. On Magazine Cut, thankfully, my cousin Baimba's gate was still closed. I would not have wanted to face him on my way to church.

We reached Kissy Road, and somehow I got lost in strange scenery. The bus stop in front of Annie Walsh School was usually a marketplace of school uniforms. The street was usually packed with people hailing taxis and lifts to work; There was usually Mr. Daramola opening his photo studio, and the Yoruba women with babies tied to their backs, putting out their merchandise of yams, waist beads, shea butter, and various grains. It must have been my first time seeing Kissy Road that devoid of life, for I found myself looking around for longer than I realized, this facade of rusty rolled-down doors and corroded bolts. By the time I pulled myself together to move on, all I could see were the backs of the family, now descending the steps into the school's gate—the same gate that led to the church's main entrance. The second group was also disappearing through the louvered swing doors that led into a second entrance.

In my five years at Trinity School, it had never occurred to me to question who uses which entrance to the church. Now that I had to enter it, I was stuck between its two entrances. Shall I follow the family down the main entrance, or shall I follow the older boys and girls in uniform through the louvered door.

Clutching the envelope in my breast pocket, I hurried toward the main entrance, then stopped, turned around, and decided the swing door entrance to which I was closest was a better way to enter. Just as I started moving in that direction, I remembered that our mock Thanksgiving service had taken us through the vestibule.

At that service, the church was on its feet when I finally staggered into the aisle. I was barely able to stand up straight when a barrage of chandelier shafts bolted toward me. The pictures of thin white men on window etchings, which I had seen several times from outside, were now alight, ricocheting against each other on either side of the room. The hymns we sang at morning assemblies were not accompanied by an organ, but at our one-time mock service, a man played the organ. Even so, I was not prepared for the pounding, like pestles on empty mortars that bolted my ears as I stood in the doorway. It was nothing like the church I used to attend from our living-room radio—a stark contrast with the naked simplicity I was used to at Mandinga Mosque.

I turned into stone on the bloody runner.

They sat down. I remained a stone. My legs began to weaken. A hand caught me. It dragged me into the closest pew. The walls began to move inside my head. They spun and spun and spun until they reached my stomach.

A hand pushed me away. "Go home."

"That's enough church for today." Attatie ignored my sobs. She shoved wood under the pot of teasoup and fanned the fire with a rusty aluminum plate. Live cinders danced up the sooty kitchen walls before exiting through a gaping casement window. "Hurry up and join your sister and brother," she continued, tucking her printed wrapper like a codepiece between her legs. Sweat beads dripped down her forehead.

I was on the cement kitchen steps still clutching my hymnal. She didn't allow our eyes to meet, so I sobbed louder and let the tears run down my uniform. I wanted her to feel the pain of the rough road ahead for me if I didn't return to the church with an adult to help clean up my vomit. How do I continue in Barbara's gang? How do I endure Mary's attacks? What do I say to Miss Jackson, leaving my vomit in that place where, if it was up to her, the entire class would spend every Sunday morning. Should I even go to school on Monday? Besides, I didn't know what happened to the brown envelope. It was no longer in my pocket when I got home. Miss Jackson would want to know.

"If you don't hurry up, maybe the cane will help you along." Her iron-spoon clanked loudly inside of the pot as she stirred together the onions, pepper, tomatoes, and liver.

Whenever I talked about my Christian friends, my mother often asked, "is she the one whose grandfather is the parson? Is she the one whose mother teaches at Cathedral school? You're making good friends." How was I to continue making good friends without the support of my family?

For Mohammed, a Thanksgiving Service was meant for Christians only, and Amie did not have Miss Jackson for a teacher. They both had the luxury of opting to be with their friends at Islamic School on a Sunday morning; my friends were at Holy Trinity Church.

I remember hating everything about my mother that morning; her headtie and wrapper; her sitting on a low kitchen bench; I hated the hand with which she stirred the breakfast soup; I hated her inability to read the Bible. All I could do about it was storm out of the kitchen declaring between sobs, that if someone didn't take me back to the church, I will not attend Islamic school again, for the rest of my life -- and with hymnal in hand, I swore to God.

"I Could've Been Somebody"

Mammy Porter had a relative who was a university professor. When he visited, he would park his Mercedes Benz within view of our veranda, which usually caused my mother to put her sewing aside for at least a few minutes. First, the professor's presence ignited a desire to show off her English.

"Good evening, Doctor Palmer. And how is de body dis evening?"

"Fine, fine," the professor would mumble.

"And how is de wife?"

"Fine, fine."

"And how is de children?"

"Fine, fine. Thank you. Everybody is fine. Thank you."

"Yes, tank you, Doctor."

As soon as the professor managed to disappear into Mammy Porter's gate, Attatie would shout for Mohammed to drop everything he was doing and immediately make his way to the veranda.

"Take a look at that car over there," she would say.

Mohammed, who had seen the car several times before and was already aware of the reason he was being ordered to look at it, would usually shrug and turn back to return to his play.

"If you don't look at that car the way I want you to look at it, things won't go right for the two of us."

When things didn't go right for you and Attatie, it meant slaps and spanks, so Mohammed usually complied.

"I've looked at it, and I like it," he would reply.

"You shouldn't just like it," my mother would say. "You should want to grow up and drive a car like that."

Mohammed would comply, although he never remembered to repeat Attatie's words the next time he was commanded to dream about Dr. Palmer's car.

For Amie and I, Mammy Penina's daughter was the hero we were commanded to want to be like. Miss Fenella went around in high heels and pencil skirts that clamped her thighs into a straight line.

"Don't you like her clothes? That's the way they dress in England." Attatie would take a break from the presser foot to speak into our eyes. "You want to go to England, don't you?"

I never needed the prodding that Mohammed elicited. I was sometimes the one to call Attatie's attention to Miss Fenella as she took precarious steps between the narrow sidewalk and the street gutter. I told her I wanted nothing more than to dress like Miss Fenella after I finished school.

"You'll have to go to England for those dresses."

"I'm going to England when I finish school."

"Then you must open your books." She would repeat the sentence in drawn-out syllables, moving from my sister's eyes to mine.

Then she would say, "You must always keep your books open."

With that, she would return to her sewing, a sign that we were free to go—open our books.

One evening, I remained standing in front of her machine after Amie had left.

"Why didn't you go to England after you finished school?" I said.

"My grandmother said it was for my own good." She kept her eyes on the presser foot. "My grandmother said a woman has to be able to respect her husband."

She finished making straight lines on the fabric, one next to the other, like white fence poles. She picked up the scissors and began zigzagging them. She had learned to embroider dresses as a teenager.

"My grandmother said Class Three education was enough for a girl."

The Chief Justice's Concubine

The girls at Trinity School often made fun of my older sister, so I avoided her like bitter syrup. She spoke as if she had a bucket of spittle in her mouth.

Some of the girls would say, "Why does your sister talk like that?" Sometimes they asked if she talked like that at home. Other times, they called on me to interpret for them—"*What did she say?*" When I got tired of interpreting, I turned to Amie and asked her several times to repeat what she had just said. Everyone copied me and asked her to repeat each word she said, and Amie would get angry and walk away. Even then, I kept a watchful eye on her.

Attatie said Amie was my responsibility. I had to produce answers as to why Amie came home without her beret, or why she got into a fight with another girl. It was hard for me to do because I would usually stay in a group separate from Amie's until we reached the junction where Magazine Cut met Goree Street. There, my mind usually began to get into the frame of home life, and I would make sure Amie and I walked together through the gate.

Everyone said Amie was short-tempered. Papa attributed it to her speech impediment, but often it was the other way around. She got angry for irrational reasons, and her speech became even more blurred.

"Go outside and spit," Papa would say.

Amie would splash several strips of spittle over the veranda's railing and returned to talk the same way.

Amie and I were playing in the living room one afternoon, when a woman appeared at our front door. She was dressed like Miss Fenella or one of the teachers at Trinity School. We cut our play and straightened up in front of her.

"Where's your mother?" she said, without a greeting.

Her reptilian eyes glared between my sister and me. There was a girl in uniform by her side who was in Amie's class, two years ahead of me.

"That's her." She pointed at Amie.

The woman charged toward Amie. "Why did you hit my daughter?"

Amie looked as though she had not yet learned how to talk.

"Answer me!" the woman shouted.

I tried to answer in Amie's place but came out blank. I had not witnessed the presumed incident. Amie had not said anything about this girl to me. Who was this strange woman shouting at my sister in the middle of our living room? My ten-year-old guts were boiling, but I was unable to act out my anger. This was an adult. And she was not just any adult. Her appearance was that of the type of woman I was being groomed to be like—my hero.

Amie began to speak, and barrels of spittle appeared to weigh down her words. I wanted to say, *Go out and spit*," but before I could talk, the girl chuckled. She was laughing at my sister, right there in our house.

"Don't say anything." I jumped in front of the woman as if to use my body to stop her mouth from opening. "Don't say anything to anyone."

I must have swiped the mother down with my eyes as I spoke, because she bristled and shouted at the top of her voice.

"Who're you looking at like that? Have you no respect for your elders?"

I thought she was going to hit me.

"Do you think I'm one of your classmates? Is that the way your mother brought you up?"

I knew not to talk back to an adult, but I could not tell her that I did not intend to wash her down with my eyes. I was too angry.

I turned to Amie instead. "Let's go and play in the backyard."

Mohammed must have heard the raised voice. The woman appeared relieved to see him. She introduced herself as Mrs. one-of-those-hyphenated-names-that-went-to-church, then gave Mohammed a message for "this un-brought-up girl's mother."

"You've just bought yourself some trouble with the government," Mohammed said, after she left. "Did you hear her name? She is the wife of the chief justice."

I didn't know what a chief justice was. I was more concerned about Attatie's reaction after hearing this belligerent woman's side of the story.

The woman did not keep her promise to return, and Amie and Mohammed backed up my story. But Attatie recognized her from my description of her attitude and dismissed the entire incident.

"The girl is the justice's daughter, all right." She chuckled. "But the justice isn't married to her mother."

Sackville Street

My mother could not yet talk when her mother died. She was raised by her mother's parents, together with their three sons and two daughters. When the uncles married, their wives came to live in the same four-bedroom bungalow on Sackville Street. It was a traditional Muslim home. They all prayed together, stooped around offerings together, and shared a pot. The wives took turns cooking for the entire family. The children ate in a circle on floor mats, dipping their hands in the same bowl.

Grandpa Karimu, the family patriarch, worked for the colonial government at Water Quay, and his wife, Siminie, sold pepper and tomatoes on a wooden table in front of the house. Both studied the Qur'an—Karimu more than Siminie—and gave their children an Islamic education until the early nineteenth century, when Anglican missionaries began building churchyard schools in the scramble to keep out of Mohammedan hands those returned Africans and former slaves.

My mother was sent to work under a Muslim seamstress who made knee-length embroidered dresses for the up-and-coming emancipated Africans. She began by learning to stitch one straight line next to the other, until every available space on a narrow piece of cloth was covered with the same color of thread. Then she learned to cut tree-like branches off the stiches to make embroidered patterns that will form the dress's bust. It was the closest to a ready-made dress you could buy in Freetown, and it was the only type of dress a Christians wore with head ties. It gave them a break from British culture without descending too deeply into the Muslim or native look.

My mother graduated from sewing school, got married, and set up her own sewing business on the veranda at Goree Street. It was her first profession with a Class Three education.

Goree Street Spies

Attatie came home one evening, after Mohammed had led us dancing around a captured bee tied onto a pole on the front yard fence.

"You stand right there," she told Mohammed.

She pointed to the center table, then lined up Amie and me next to Mohammed.

"What did I tell you before I left?"

She was addressing Mohammed, but her rugged tone had me worried. I rubbed a hand on my tender eyebrow. It felt moist, but there was no blood on my fingers. I felt safe.

"What do I always tell you before I go out?"

"I didn't do anything wrong." Mohammed pointed to the back door. "We all stayed in the backyard, playing."

I bobbed my in panic-stricken nods of agreement.

"What's that on your brow?"

I don't think she even looked at my forehead as she spoke. Her mind was on the hand she had ducked between the cushions of her chair. I cringed. I knew what she was looking for.

Amie and I had spat on the tips of our index fingers and touched our foreheads to promise Mohammed we wouldn't mention anything about the incident. My fourteen-year-old brother was next to God. He could crouch under the veranda railing and describe any car that passed on Goree Street.

"Blue Peugeot! Black Opel! Red Renault!"

He got them all right, so I believed in his claims to kill or maim any person or animal in his way.

"Who tied the bee to the fence?" Attatie said.

I felt my world capsize. My face was flooding with sweat.

"I didn't do anything." Mohammed's voice cracked, but his face was dry.

"We didn't do anything." Amie was tearing up.

"Yes, we didn't do anything," I said, between tears.

I was convinced Attatie was guessing. After all, she wasn't there when Mohammed caught the bee.

"Someone is telling a lie about us." Mohammed moaned. "I wish I knew who that is."

"Yes." I sobbed. "They're telling a lie."

Attatie bristled. Our sobs loudened as we watched her enter her bedroom and return with a cane.

"Who tied the bee to the iron pole?" she repeated to Mohammed. There was silence until she pointed the cane at my eyebrow.

"What's that mark on your forehead?"

"I didn't do it," Mohammed replied.

"There's nothing on my forehead, Ma," I said with confidence.

Mohammed had told me the iodine would erase all signs of the wound. He killed a pigeon with his catapult once and shared the meat with us. He removed Fatmata's feeding bottle from between her teeth and tucked some of the meat in her mouth. She chewed contentedly and helped it down with her milk. Amie and I sent ours down with water from the backyard drum. There was nothing Mohammed couldn't fix. Besides, Attatie could not have seen the blood dripping down my face. She couldn't have been lurking around in some corner, watching me hit my forehead against the iron pole as I tried to escape the trapped bee.

Attatie raised the cane above my head, and I cracked.

"Mohammed let the bee go," I said. "We didn't play with it."

"Yes," Amie said. "As soon as he caught it, he let it go."

"What bee?" Attatie's first stroke landed on Mohammed's head. "What do I always tell you before leaving the house?"

"To stay with my sisters on the veranda." Mohammed began to sob.

I looked around, unsuccessfully, for an escape route. When the first stroke landed on my shoulder, I felt a fresh sting of iodine on my eyebrow.

"Mammy Penina has no reason to tell a lie on you," Attatie said.

The strokes were flying around us, landing on Mohammed's head, Amie's face, my shoulders, before swiping off to return with even greater force.

Mammy Penina!

Mohammed had rushed me inside the house after the blood started dripping down my face. How could she have seen anything?

My siblings and I were not the only children within the narrow confines of the neighborhood, but I used to believe that these grandmothers sat on their windowsills all day just to admire us when we played. From that day, Mohammed taught Amie and I to call them witches and Attatie's spies, and made sure that when our parents were away, we confined our play to the backyard or the parlor, free from their prying eyes.

Fetching Water

We had no pump in our yard, but since we were not natives or people from up country, my mother relegated the task of filling the two backyard drums to the houseboy. It went well until the dry season, Friday, when the houseboy had to be away for the weekend on an urgent family matter.

"Amie and I will do it!" I said, looking forward to my debut at the street pump.

Amie, too, was enthusiastic.

"No," Attatie replied. "Lamina will have to walk faster and fill both drums before he leaves."

Lamina, however, dilly-dallied, took his time sweeping the yard, ambled to the street pump and back, and at the end of the day, filled only one drum.

"That backward countryman," Attatie said. "His eyes are opening up too fast."

So early on Saturday morning, Amie and I washed our faces and began running around the yard, looking for the right sized pails for ten- and twelve-year-olds. We also got old rags to cushion our heads.

My mind was racing, along with my legs. *Not only will I sit in the middle of Goree Street, but I will carry my pail like children do coming from the street pump. I will balance it on my head, gesturing with my free hands, turning my head this way and that. I'll carry water all day Saturday, all day Sunday, and maybe Attatie will even let me carry water in the evenings after school. What fun I'll have! Soon, I will be allowed to fetch water, even under the rain. I will leave my pail beside the pump for the rain to fill. Meanwhile, I will take off my clothes and dance in my panties up and down Goree Street. I'll dance under the crackling of*

*thunder and splash of lightning, even against the hollering of Mammy Penina and
Ma Abel from their window and porch.*

"You'll fetch water only from Mammy Penina's house," Attatie
said.

I really wanted to join the children at the street pump, but it was
either I went along with her condition, or I didn't fetch water at all. At
least I was getting an entry into the daring world of fetching water. I
could still balance the kettle on my head, on the walkway from Mammy
Penina's yard into Goree Street, and even on the dirt ground from our
veranda to the backyard.

"Yes, Ma." I grabbed my kettle. "I'll only go to Mammy Penina's
yard."

Amie also promised.

Naturally, Mammy Penina was not in her backyard. She lived by
her window, after all. I didn't expect to see Miss Fenella—who had
been to England—hanging around the backyard in her pencil skirt,
trying to put a pot on the fire. It was a barren, cemented yard, except
for an elderly woman sitting on a low wooden bench, separating sorrel
leaves from their stalk. No items were around her that I associated
with a backyard. No pots and pans on dirt ground. No rickety wicker
basket lying around. No mortar on the ground. No pencil against the
kitchen panel. There were not even the turned-out pages of used exercise books that littered our yard. No pink-skinned body parts from
plastic dolls. None of the rusty milk tins we played with, Mohammed's
catapult, or the stones and faggots around it.

The woman probably noticed my clutched knuckles over the pail
handle, and Amie's disoriented look as we tried to introduce ourselves.

"You've come to get water?" She pointed to the pump before we
could respond.

It looked ornamental, enclosed in a dry, roomy cemented space,
with a bulky, high brick under the spout on which to sit a pail.

"We shouldn't spill water here," I whispered to Amie, as I inched
my pail on the brick and turned the spigot as if it were an egg. Amie
nodded and covered her mouth to snicker. I started to wipe off the
water that splattered on the dry cement walls with my cushion rag, but
Amie laughed at me, and so I stopped.

My pail filled up, and with Amie's help, I pulled it up to rest on the parapet. While Amie's pail was filling, I wrapped the rag around my hand into a tight circle, the way the houseboy usually did, then set it on my head before squatting to grab each end of the pail's handle. As soon as I slanted my head forward to pick up the pail, the pad loosened and fell to the ground.

"Let me do it for you." Amie held the pad on my head while I brought the pail to bear on it.

Now, I stood with the bucket on my head, waiting for Amie's to fill. It filled up, and we both stood erect, like sheep looking at the woman as if she were salt. A few minutes passed before she happened to look our way, and we still couldn't utter a word, until she got up and came to our rescue.

"Thank you, Ma," we chorused, as she helped the bucket onto Amie's padded head.

The pail produced only a slight tension against my skull plate, as if I carried a heavy bundle of clothes. I felt brave. Amie and I exchanged smiles. We belonged to that group of fearless children who fetched water every day. Those children who seldom listened to adults. Those children with parents buried too deep in the struggles of everyday life to hover around their children.

In our newly achieved fearless state, we ventured out of Mammy Penina's gate and approached the narrow courtyard that separated her boundary from Mammy Porter's. It ran into two steps that led to the street gutter. There, I decided to balance the pail on my head and free my hands.

"Attatie does not have to pay anyone to fetch water." I flipped out my palms. "We can do it as well as…"

I turned to face Amie, and the pail turned the other direction and slid off my head, taking the padding cloth with it as it clattered on the concrete.

Attatie called Amie and I to the living room later that evening, after, miraculously, allowing me to change out of my wet clothes without much questioning, and continue fetching water until the drum was half-full.

"Now, sit where I can see your eyes," Attatie said.

Mammy Penina again. Even without a window into the courtyard, those witch's eyes had seen me waste a bucket of water out of pure playfulness.

"Look me in the eye," Attatie said, drilling hers into mine.

I had some of my scariest moments when my mother demanded I look into her eyes. The darker skin around her eyes sank her pupils into a depth that could sting.

"How many times did you go to Mammy Penina's yard today?"

I counted on my fingers the number of times I stood on the steps in front of the gutter, waiting for a car to pass.

"Five times?" I looked toward Amie.

"Six times?" she said.

We went back and forth six times or seven times, before Attatie interrupted.

"Did you see any papers in Mammy Penina's yard?"

I was quick to answer, but the questions continued too quickly.

"Did you see any pencils lying around? Did you see any empty tins in the yard? Did you see any dolls lying around? Wouldn't you be proud to bring your friends home if your backyard looked like that? Don't you want our backyard to look like that?

Amie and I nodded, but I hadn't a clue how I was going to cement our backyard and keep it spotless.

A Girl to Lead Prayers

I changed from my Trinity School uniform into a long dress for Islamic School. It was a school-day routine, followed by the walk -- a usually boisterous social event. On Goree Street, someone would snatch the Qur'an from my armpit and run with it.

"The Qur'an is not a book you play with." I would repeat Alpha Ghazali's admonition, before taking off after the offender.

I got my Qur'an back and yanked an exercise book. The owner would come after me. Someone would yank Amie's head-tie, and on and on, until we found ourselves in the company of the Conteh children a few houses down the street. Ahmed, Marie, and Umu emerged from their two-room house, with their Qur'ans.

We laughed and chatted on, until we reached Ahmadiyya Mosque, where we brought our fingers to our lips for a minute or two of respect. Then we stopped to adorn our head ties with hibiscus from Mrs. Dixon's garden and appeased her by buying ginger cakes and peppermint sweets from her sidewalk stall. The Kallay boys joined us a few minutes later. Theirs was a spacious pawpaw-colored house with a narrow yard that led to several small one- and two-room apartments that extended backward into Jenkins Street. Mr. Kallay, his wife, and sons occupied the big house. Snotty toddlers and their half-naked older siblings played in the yard.

Mr. Kallay was also landlord of the sweet shop next door, where the Fullah man who sometimes presided over offerings at our house lived. He ran a school on the steps of the store, with eight or ten boys chanting qur'anic verses scripted on wooden tablets, while the teacher's cane dangled over the counter.

We would stand in front of the boys and laugh at the way they read. At our school, we were taught to merge our syllables. We read, *Bis-mi-lahi-rah-mani-ra-him*. These boys read, *Bi-a-si-mi-la-hi a-ra-aha-ma-ni-a-ra-hi-mi*. So country!

The group from Goree Street would balloon at Fourah Bay Road and arrive at the school like a thunder bolt. Together, with Mohammed, Amie and I, and the Conteh and Kallay children, there was Leah and Fatmata Ghazali, Tejan and Alieu Kallay, Kadi Mansaray, Mari Conteh, Adama Sillah, Marie Kamara, Umu Sillah, Jarieu Sillah, Feremusu, Abdul Karim Lamin, and Mari Kudah. We scattered on the streets like locusts. Girls in long dresses and head scarfs. Boys in long kaftans and fez caps. All of us carrying Qur'ans in varying states of bad preservation.

Our voices usually preceded us into the house of one of our teachers who lived across the street from the mosque. Alpha Yansaneh would appear at his gate, looking like someone pulled out of bed in a hurry. He would stand, legs apart, in the middle of the street and flap his hands up and down to motion quietness. The result was always disastrous. We would kiss our kneecaps in laughter, and the boys would tease him further by running toward him, and just as he was about to snatch their shirts, whisk right past him, toward Dove Cut Wharf. It was only after we had satisfied our playful whims, or Alpha Yansaneh threatened us with the name Alpha Ghazali, that we collected ourselves and headed for the schoolyard.

The sun was usually behind us when Alpha Ghazali arrived in the classroom. His presence was like a whip. It sobered up every class. Most times, he arrived in time to line up the entire school into the mosque for Maghrib prayers. Other times, it was only the boys. And sometimes, only the girls that he took into the mosque.

There was a power cut one evening that ran into the Magrib hour. Alpha Ghazali hurried into the dark schoolroom and headed for the girls' section.

"We're too late to go into the mosque." He picked up a flaming candle. "I need a volunteer to lead us in classroom prayers."

I counted myself out. Leading prayers was a task for older boys like Mohammed and Tejan. *Alpha Ghazali is standing in the girls' section, but surely the older boys can hear him.*

He made a second and a third call, with no takers.

"Is Fatmata here?"

Fatmata did not answer her father.

"Is Leah here?"

She did not answer, either.

We were under candlelight, so I could not see Alpha Ghazali's face. But when he walked past the row in which I sat, I sensed trouble. He reached the row where his firstborn daughter sat on a long wooden desk-and-chair combo that held about four or five other girls. Fatmata was already in fits as she trotted behind her father like a roped cow, the gathers of her long dress in the same hand as her father's whip.

Alpha Ghazali took his time replacing the candle on the teacher's desk, and slowly poured its hot glue on the tabletop before sticking the candle base erect atop the firming liquid. Alpha Yansaneh watched like a leaf under the harmattan breeze.

The dancing and singing Alpha Ghazali usually encouraged did not interfere with his imperative to teach, and ours to learn. He had little patience for slackness, which for him meant a lack of enthusiasm for Islamic studies. It was not unusual for Alpha Ghazali, at such a time when we were singing and dancing, to spin his smiles into a spank on the shoulder of an infractious child.

Leah was now jumping up and down the aisle, shouting her belated offer to lead prayers. The desperation in her voice was more sobering than the swishing of the whip on her older sister's body. From under the desks, we all endured the end of Fatmata's whipping, and the beginning of Leah's.

Out on the schoolyard, I rubbed Leah's arms, hoping to erase the mark I could not see in the dark. Everyone surrounded Leah and Fatmata.

"Hush, Leah. Hush, Fatmata."

The boys joined us. "Hush, Leah. Hush, Fatmata."

Alpha Yansaneh came out and shooed us homeward. Everyone followed his orders without a sound.

The Rent Money

It used to happen every now and then. Sometimes it was a cup of water offered to Attatie's departed grandmother, asking for safety on the roads, or help for the children during an exam. At other times, there was food and clothing, kolanuts and coins in a glass of water, and that mix of seeds and grains she called *fangadama* - to request help from Allah and the ancestors for a larger problem. Then the curse came, and the offerings became constant.

Attatie was sitting on the morris chair, feeding her new baby, Hassana. Mr. Conteh was standing on the veranda, dressed in his white pharmacist coat.

"I've told you already." Mr. Conteh said. "I have given you the rent."

"No, you didn't," Attatie replied.

"I swear on my Qur'an." He raised his voice. "You were sewing on the veranda when I gave you the rent."

"I don't care about your Qur'an." Attatie raised hers, too. "You didn't give it to me."

"I said I gave it to you."

"I say you didn't."

"Check your handbag. Check everywhere you put money."

"I've checked everywhere. I do not have the rent."

"Would I tell a lie?"

"You *are* telling a lie."

Mr. Conteh returned to his apartment, and Attatie sucked her teeth.

The two-bedroom ranch we lived in was one of three houses my grandfather owned by the time he died at age forty-five. There was a

one-bedroom apartment adjoined to it, which Granny assigned to her
nephew Mr. Conteh and allowed Papa to collect the rent.

Mr. Conteh was an avid football fan who taught me the names
of every player on the East End Lions. On returning from a game, he
would call my siblings and me to the veranda and kick an imaginary
football to demonstrate how King Kama Dumbuya's scored a goal.
He showed us how Christian Cole kicked the ball to Abu Syrian, or
to Manneh Peters, or to Vava George. On days when his work at the
pharmacy prevented him from attending a game, he would slump in
a chair on the veranda, pipe in mouth, and keep the neighborhood
abreast of the game with his shrieks over the raspy radio waves.

"Here. Go buy a pint of Coca-Cola for everyone," he would tell
Mohammed, when the East End Lions won.

When they lost to their archrival, The Mighty Blackpool, it was
our fault.

"You children cause too much noise," he would complain, before
reducing the radio's volume to a static whisper and disappearing into
his apartment.

It was after a loss by the East End Lions that Attatie dared confront Mr. Conteh a second time, about the rent.

He pointed a vicious finger toward the sky. "I gave you the rent,
and you said I didn't. Allah will judge between us."

"Allah is for all of us," Attatie quipped.

"I'm moving out!" he yelled.

"That's good. You're too loud, anyway. You make too much noise."

"You mean, I should not talk."

"You should talk like someone civilized. Not like someone from
up country." Attatie counted his sins on her fingers. "The other day,
when the car overturned up the road, you shouted so hard you woke
up the baby. Then when you listen to the game on the radio, your voice
is louder than the radio. Your voice is so loud I cannot sleep, even
when I have a headache."

"OK, I will go," Mr. Conteh replied. "And leave you with your
good-for-nothing son.

Attatie did not respond to that one.

"By the grace of Allah, he will not amount to anything."

***

Not a day passed that Attatie did not mention, within Papa's hearing, the curse that Mr. Conteh had placed on her only son. A man, Papa's own cousin, that Papa's own mother had brought amongst us. Papa atoned by being present at every offering Attatie made to ward off Mr. Conteh's curse. Mohammed was reminded, often with a slap across his face, of the forces working toward his destruction, and Amie and I were dared to forget we were next in line after our brother was eviscerated. Worse, at eight years old, I lost the only dress that put me in vogue.

When the altered top fashion came to Freetown, Attatie said, "We're Marabous. We don't dress like that."

Then she tried to appease me with the assurance I would be able to wear it after I had finished school and returned from England.

The altered top later took on thin straps. Attatie bought a fabric of blue hibiscus and made one of her apprentices sew Amie and I the new style, with thick straps and a high neckline. I wore it to Ilakow, to Granny's house, and even attempted to wear it at home. In my eyes, it was still a new dress, when Attatie barricaded my bedroom door with her body and said, "Bring me that dress with the thin straps."

The fight had started with Mohammed.

"Bring me one of your shirts," she said.

"I don't have any more shirts," Mohammed shouted back from the bedroom the three of us shared. "You've used all of my shirt and trousers in your offerings."

He was passing the age of fear, and he was beginning to stand up, if ordered to sit, and thought nothing of the stench from his shoes.

"*Alakie!*" Attatie shouted. "Ingratiate! Good for nothing! Amadu Conteh was right about you."

"I never asked for your sacrifices. I don't want them. You always—"

Mohammed was lying on his back, but before he could finish his words, Attatie was in the bedroom. He rushed to straighten up for the slap that was coming, then realized that Attatie had other plans.

"Clear out!" she shouted, as mother and son met on the lock of the metal box where Mohammed kept his clothes.

Mother's elbow was already jammed against her son's chest. While Mohammed sat on the floor, howling, Attatie jerked out a pair of trousers and shirt before leaving the room.

I had been working feverishly myself, pushing my strapped dress down the bottom of my portmanteau. When she returned for me, I held out one of those frocks that went past my knees. She held it in one hand, like a clothes hanger, and inspected it from all sides before throwing it back at me.

"This one is turned in the arms. "I want a dress I can give away."

"Let me check amongst the laundry," I murmured.

"What about the blue dress. We can give it away now. You've worn it enough."

I knew not to argue with her. I made two timid backward steps to ensure enough room between us as I dug into the portmanteau, shuffled through the top rows of clothes, folding back each dress I had unfolded, and ensuring I took my time reaching the box's bottom. Of course, she saw through my plans and shoved me aside to dig to the bottom of the portmanteau.

"That's a new dress," was all I could say when she pulled out my favorite blue dress.

"It's not new anymore," she snapped, before turning her attention to Amie, who she later left in as much distress as Mohammed and me.

"Bring your *alakie* selves out here."

I entered the living room, muttering words under my breath. Attatie and Papa were sitting on the linoleum, together with one of her sewing apprentices. The teacher from the doorstep Islamic school at the bottom of Goree Street was arriving, flanked by his pupils in soiled kaftans and muddy feet. There was such a scramble to carve stooping spots closest to the rice and fish stew bowls that the teacher had to remind them, "You read first. Then you can eat."

Attatie waved a violent hand across their faces. "C'mon. Push back. Push back."

And the fowl fluttered from slumber, under the breeze her heavy hand left behind.

Before the offering could start, Attatie command all three of us to acknowledge the items to be sacrificed. I didn't mind touching the fowl on its head, touching the rim of each bowl of rice and fish stew, the glass holding the water and kola nuts, the mélange of grains and shelled groundnuts atop pieces of red, white, and black fabric. None of it was as painful as having to make an impersonal touch-and-go contact with a favorite dress I was about to lose. I acknowledged neither my dress, nor in solidarity with them, Amie's or Mohammed's. They followed my lead and acknowledged all the items except the clothes. Either Attatie had decided to pick her battles, or we had worn her out, but she did not react, and the teacher went ahead and acknowledged the bulk of the items with a quick motion of his thin arm in the air above them, then began his quar'anic recitals.

Everyone murmured, "Ameena! Ameena! Ameena!" as the teacher read.

Attatie whispered, "Ameena," and picked up a groundnut, cracked its shell and threw it back into the bunch, fingered the grains this way and that, lifted the edges of the clothing pile as though counting to make sure they were all there, and ducked a finger in the glass of kola nuts, all the while, watching intermittently to make sure our lips were moving. Then she began to summon the ancestors.

"My mother and father, Mameh Sillah and Mustapha Conteh, my grandmother and grandfather, Siminie Sillah and Karimu Sillah, in Allah's name, do not sit by and allow a bad person to put a curse on your grandson. Continue to watch over your grandchildren. Intervene on their behalf. Stay with us. Do not stray far from me."

The prayers ended, and Attatie folded Mohammed's shirt and put it on the teacher's lap, then she put my dress on the floor next to the apprentice. While the boys devoured the rice and fish stew, she stacked the red, white, and black fabric, one on top of the other, poured the grains and groundnuts into them, then gave the bundle to the apprentice.

"Take it away," she said, "and scatter it at the four road."

The apprentice nodded, a grave expression on her face, and turned to go.

Attatie wiped her hands down her cotton wrapper and said to herself, "Scatter it right at the spot where Goree Street meets Bombay Street. Scatter it the way his curse on my son will shatter."

***

How could I take sides in a battle between my mother and my uncle? Mr. Conteh was fun to be around, like a much older brother, but he had left me scared. Attatie had said his curse could turn Mohammed into the irrevocably ruined Abi-laabi that Alpha Ghazali was fond of describing to us at Ilakow.

"He disobeyed Allah, so everything he touched turned bad," Alpha Ghazali would remind us. "Even his wife's jewelry, when he touched it, turned into stone."

I doted on Mohammed too much then, to see him become like Abi-laabi.

As long as I was not losing another dress, and Papa had promised me a new one just like the one I lost, I resolved to put up with the stench from rotten leaves and black liquid my mother sprayed in the house every day, and watched patiently every Sunday as hungry boys and girls devoured rice and fish or chicken stew, or oranges, bananas, milk and honey—whatever the old medium instructed—and prayed Miss Jackson or one of my friends did not suddenly turn up in my house during those offerings.

But I had to draw the line somewhere. If my mother had her way, I would go to school smelling like a witch doctor's daughter.

"It's for your own good." She tried to put the dark bottle of *antrul* in my hand.

The decomposed leaves had been reduced to a stenchy smell I knew very well. I do not think she missed the horror on my face or the firmness of my hands in akimbo. She simply ignored them.

"I've added perfume to it," she said, cheerfully removing the ce-ment-paper cap.

She poured some of the liquid in her cupped hand and brought it to my nose. I was standing naked to my panties, in the bedroom she and Papa shared. It did not smell like perfume to me.

"I do not want to go to school smelling like that," I replied.

"Your friends will smell only the perfume."

"No, it smells bad."

"It will protect you from bad people."

"My friends are not bad people."

"No, they're not, but there are bad people around. Some of your father's relatives do not want you and your sisters and brother to amount to anything. This will protect you from them."

"My friends will laugh at me," I said. "They will say I'm a native."

"Your friends don't have a mother like me. None of their mothers can care for you the way I do."

I shook my head. I wanted neither to understand, nor wish to contrast my mother's caring with that of another parent. All I knew was I didn't want to be called native. I didn't want to lose my friends, who were mostly Christians, and the kind of girls our teachers cared most about.

"If you have any sense," her pupils widened, "you'll beg me to do things like this for you."

"But the girls in school do not rub those things on their bodies," I pleaded, knowing she was getting angry.

"*Pshoo.*" She turned her face toward the door as if speaking to someone standing there. "This is why my grandfather used to say children have no sense. They are the stupidest of Allah's creation."

The recalling of her grandfather's maxim relieved her some. She returned to me and poured a replacement to the liquid which had been dripping from her hand.

"Just rub a little bit only on your face. I promise, you won't smell bad amongst your friends."

"Even a little bit smells." I turned to end the conversation and get my uniform from the bed.

The unwelcomed wet and smelly splash hit my back as I bent down to pick up the uniform. It trickled down all the way into the opening in my behind.

"I'm not going to wear that smelly thing to school," I shouted, and rushed out of the room to wash the liquid off my back.

"Children have no sense," my mother kept repeating to herself.

Stepping On It

I was coming home from school with a group of girls, when we came across a tiny mound of red cloth at the four-road of Kissy Road and Magazine Cut. A girl named Annie Brown first saw it.

"Don't step on it!" she shouted, holding us back with a bitty hand.

"Don't go that way," Cassandra said.

We hopped and tiptoed to avoid stepping on even a solitary grain of the *fangadama*. Of course, it was a familiar sight to me, but I rope-walked with the group and jumped over every rice, corn, and sesame grain that the red cloth uncovered on the hot tar.

"It's those natives," Annie grumbled.

I agreed.

"They make our streets dirty with their witchcraft," Cassandra said.

I agreed, my mind returning to the offering in our living room, and my mother's passionate instructions to the apprentice on how to dispose of the *fangadama*, when a girl touched my arm and shouted, "You stepped on the corn!"

"You're going to die." Annie giggled.

I made a reflective jump, taking most of the others with me in the narrow escape from the depth of the filthy street gutter. Our screams and loud laughter attracted other groups of girls coming out of the school compound. It was now a carnival of shrieks and scuffles on Magazine Cut. Everyone was made aware of the presence of the *fangadma*, and we pushed and shoved each other, trying to avoid the spread, and bumped against adult passerbys, who pushed us back with hisses and rebukes of, "Rude school pikin dem."

The Children of Lungi

When Papa was a junior civil servant at the Ministry of Lands, his job included battling snakes and crocodiles in swampy up-country waters to make roads for government projects. He went into virgin territories in Makeni, Kabala, Kono, Port-Loko, with ten cutlass-toting men to cut bushes and survey lands for roads, schools, and hospitals. His last station before he was promoted to a permanent office job in the city was at Lungi, a forty-minute ferry ride from Freetown. I saw him only on weekends when he visited, but we made a one-day trip to Lungi one Sunday.

Attatie got up early to prepare the rice and beef stew and packed soft drinks for the trip. Aunty Olay carried Fatmata, who was then a toddler, in the front seat of the taxicab to the Targrin port, and my two siblings and I sat with Attatie at the back.

It was my first ferry ride, and I spent the entire trip under my mother's wrapper, until I was hurled onto Lamina's lanky shoulder to cross the ramp to the nearby taxi where Papa awaited with Daddy Sahr, another of his men. On the rickety taxi ride to Papa's bungalow, we bounced in and out of potholes as naked children with swollen bellies waved to us in front of mud huts as though we were tourists.

As soon as the taxis stopped in front of Papa's bungalow—the only house without a thatched roof—several barefooted children with varying stomach sizes began assembling in front of the house to stare, first at the taxis, and after the taxis left, at us. They devoured us like food.

"C'mon, shoo." I waved at them.

"Are nor wan see no dorty pikin here," Attatie said.

Daddy Sahr, as he was leaving with Lamina, pulled some away with him, but they were back almost before the red dust from under his feet had resettled. Mohammed made a rush move that spread a thick screen of dust between us and the children. Again, they moved backward, only long enough for the dust to clear. Then they leaned on one another's dust-papered shoulder and stared wide-eyed at the sight of the *city* in front of them.

It got worse when Attatie brought out the food. Papa's bungalow had only one bedroom and a living room furnished with a small table stacked with drafting papers, a bulky calculator, geometry rulers, pens, and pencils. On the other end of the table were covered dishes, a plate, and other kitchen utensils. After we had rested a few minutes, he cleared out the work area of the table and brought it onto the cement paving outside. Attatie served Amie and me first. We sat on a thin bench, placed our bowl of rice and beef stew between us on the bench, and dipped our fingers in. Mohammed was seated on the door's threshold, with his fingers rested inside his bowl. Papa was served next, on a plate with a spoon. And next to him, Attatie and Aunty Olay dipped their fingers in the same bowl on the table.

Some of the children came so close that Attatie had to pick up a small stick.

"I want no dirty pikin here."

But they only stared as they held onto each other's arms and rubbed against each other's skin, and ambled only a few yards back until we finished eating. Attatie separated them into three groups. They all sat on the red dirt. To one group, she gave the leftovers from Amie and me. To the second group, she gave Papa's leftovers. And to the third, she gave hers and Aunty Olay's. Mohammed had no leftovers.

Papa and Attatie went inside to relax after lunch and Aunty Olay stayed with us outside. Daddy Sahr returned with Lamina and a dark, hefty colleague named Money Palaver. They brought us gifts of mangos, which we ate as they entertained us with stories about their encounter with city people at a time when they were still *green*, or when they could not speak or understand Krio.

Money Palaver told us about the first time he picked up the telephone in Papa's office. He had been living in the city for only a few months, and even though his Krio was improving, he spoke or under-stood very little English.

"Hello," he heard someone say.

"Hello," he repeated.

"Who's speaking?" the voice said.

As Money repeated the words *who's speaking*, the copper color of his face grew dark.

"I was badly offended by the question," he said. "I'm nobody's pikin."

So he replied to the caller, "Whose pikin? Me no pikin. Me ol' man. Me get white hair."

It was the first and last time, he said, that he touched that tele-phone thing, in Papa's office or anywhere else.

"People in Freetown have no respect for those that saw the moon before them."

The Brother from Up-Country

I came home from school to a strong stench on the backyard steps. Had my uniform picked up something from the school latrine? Before I could look further, my mother pointed to a raggedy bundle at the foot of the steps.

"This is your new brother."

It was an image even the boys at the bottom of Goree Street would have shunned. A dense cloud of knotted hair sat on his head. It stored a stench that powdered the open shirt and rolled up trousers tenting his elementary-school frame.

"I don't want him for my brother," I snapped.

"But he's going to help us around the house," Attatie said. "He'll fetch water, pound pepper, and sweep the floor so you don't have to do those things."

"I never do those things!" I yelled.

She never even allowed us to fetch water, ever since that weekend I splashed water on myself.

"You will soon if we don't have this boy to help."

"But we have a houseboy."

"The houseboy's eyes are opening up too fast," she sneered.

"I don't mind fetching water," I said.

As for pounding pepper and onions, I longed to perform the dexterous act Miss Tor sometimes displayed for our entertainment—to pound a few strokes, throw the pestle up in the air, clap two or three times, and without missing a beat, catch the pestle and continue pounding. But Attatie said women like Miss Fenella didn't pound onions.

Where's he going to sleep?" I said in a triumphant tone.

We had only two rooms: Papa and Attatie's, and the room that Amie, Mohammed, and I shared. Surely Mohammed would not share his bed with a smelly country boy.

"He's used to sleeping on the floor," Attatie replied.

"I don't mind him helping in the house, but he cannot live with us, and he cannot be my brother."

It was settled that the little boy from up-country was not my brother, but he was going to stay, after Attatie sketched a family tree that placed Abassy's father among the children of one of her grandmother's relatives.

For several weeks, our bedroom, and even my school uniform, took on the smell of rotten leaves that Attatie had been trying to stamp on my body.

Looking the Road for the Rice Business

The young female sewing apprentices who reported for work at our house every day helped to feed Fatmata, babysat us, ran errands to Bombay Street market, checked the water on the boiling rice, and swept the veranda, all while learning to make straight stiches on a cloth, before graduating to cutting and sewing the embroidered print dresses. Of course, it didn't help that the houseboy's eyes were showing no signs of returning to its native state.

Attatie had just begun the process of cleansing Mr. Conteh's old apartment. The old man she brought in crawled into a reed mat Attatie had spread in the vacant room and set his raffia bag next to him. I stood on the threshold, waiting for my mother's approval.

"Come in if you're coming in," she said. "Otherwise, go out and close the door."

I stepped in, closed the door, and sat next to my mother at the edge of the mat, face-to-face with a pair of wrinkled legs halted by feet like burnt pancakes.

"Pa," Attatie said. "I want this place cleaned." She looked at the zinc panels as though they had intestines. "I know Amadu Conteh is still in here." She X-rayed the ceiling and windowsill. "I want to remove his presence from these rooms."

Pa opened a small drawstring cloth from his raffia bag and cupped its contents in his hands. He shook it like someone eager to make a killing at a casino table, before gently spreading out the pebbles onto the mat. With his fingertips, he changed the shapes of the pebbles: circles, triangles, rectangles, figure eights. He rubbed his chin, bent his head this way and that. Picked up one or two of the pebbles, held them a few moments away from the rest, put them back, touched a pair, moved it to one side, up, below, left, right. He picked up another set and rubbed it between his palms. Finally, he brought all the stones back together to start the separation and observation all over again. He did this about three times, before the items needed for the offering emerged: one red and one white kola nut floating inside a glass of water; a yard each of red, black, and white satin cloth; sesame, corn, and rice mix; two or three bowls of cooked rice and fish stew to be eaten by hungry children. The stew should be hidden under the rice to create an element of surprise. A pleasant surprise the poor children will experience when they find out they are not about to eat just plain rice. A sweet inverse to Mr. Conteh's disappointment when he finds out his plans have been preempted, and Mohammed turns out the opposite of Mr. Conteh's curse.

I was already accustomed to, or rather, dreaded, the instructions for the cloths and sesame mix—scatter them on the spot where two roads become four. By the time Pa was ordering the kola nuts be given to older adults, and the water thrown on the front and back thresholds of our house, I was already panicking over my friends and I stepping on the *fangadama* mix. God knows where the apprentice will throw this one.

"I want you to look to the road ahead for my interest in the rice business." Attatie was already moving on, after having committed Pa's instructions to memory. "Should I put money in it? Is it right for me?"

Pa consulted his pebbles again and brought forth the offering for a successful career in the rice business. One large goat, a costly garment, two dozen bowls of rice and beef stew. Pa's orders were carried out within days, and soon the key to Mr. Conteh's old living room was amongst the extra bobbin cases and thread spools inside of Attatie's sewing machine pouch.

"Would you like to see a sample of my rice?" she said. "I have the best prices in town."

The women who came to have dresses made now left with a bag of rice or a deposit for one. Passerbys on Goree Street heard a similar pitch.

"How de body? How de pikin dem? Thank God for that. My health is good, too. Thank you. My children doing well, too. Have you bought your rice yet? I sell twenty-pound bags. Imported. Come take a look. I have the best price."

Grandpa Fabilo

It was one of Papa's many uncles who opened Attatie's eyes to a new profession. Grandpa Fabilo was a tall, majestic Mandinga with high jawbones and a pair of active eyes. He was a rice agent. When Attatie took Amie and me to visit at his rice store at Fourah Bay Road, we would sit on benches under enormous burlap bags and watch the cars go by while they talked about the rice business. He saw in my mother, qualities that she probably did not yet recognize in herself. He gave Attatie receipts for rice he had purchased at wholesale price. Attatie took delivery of the merchandise and retailed them, kept the profit and returned the capital to Grandpa Fabilo.

We never left Grandpa Fabilo's store without something for lunch, a few shillings, or even a pound each. The real treat came when we visited at his brick house at the top of Goree Street. He would sit Amie and me on the bed, pull up his long kaftan and go down on his knees. We pinched our palms in gleeful anticipation as he unlocked the metal bolts of my first association with a bank—a large steel portmanteau he kept under his bed. It contained endless piles of notes next to countless rows of coins stacked one on top of another. He would grab a handful of bills from a pile, and without bothering to count them, put a stack in my hand, and another in Amie's. There were times when he wouldn't bother picking up the bills himself.

"Take as much as you want," he would say.

I remember Mohammed telling me papers bought more toffee than coins, so before long, I began going for the papers.

The Omole Bar

When an old cook came to work for us, Attatie insisted we call her *Granny*.

Granny Kadi was a short, beefy woman in her fifties, with a face that appeared to have been cut out of a copper coin. A hired cook for weddings, funerals, and other social events, Granny Kadi began working for us as a day cook, with the understanding that she took days off for her big-event jobs. At such times, she would return in the evening with goodies—jollof rice, peppered chicken, cake and rice bread—which my siblings and I devoured while she gossiped about people we did not know. Our visit to Granny's house on Boyle Street, which was already much reduced because of school and Ilakow, became even fewer with Granny Kadi's presence at home.

When my mother gave birth to twins, Hassana and Alusine, and Alusine returned to buy salt within a few hours of birth, Granny Kadi made sure Hassana had a reason to stay. She rose early in the morning following the baby's homecoming and cooked a large pot of black-eyed beans in palm oil sauce. She put baby and bowl of beans on a large fanner and carried it on her head. Now, she lined up my sisters and I behind her and circled the house, singing and dancing, swinging baby and beans in the fanner. We clapped and mimicked her movements and mouthed the Soso songs she ululated. Afterwards, we sat with her in the backyard to eat the beans out of the fanner, with the baby looking on and looking forward, Granny Kadi said, to the day she would be old enough to join in the fun of eating every twin child's favorite dish.

By the time the baby was, what Attatie called, *strong*, Granny Kadi had moved into Mr. Conteh's old bedroom. Granny Kadi prayed and

fasted with us, and if Attatie had to go out, baby sat us when we returned from school. Usually, as soon as her duties were complete, she
bathed, spread white powder on her neck and chest, dressed up, and
went to spend the evening with a friend at the bottom of Goree Street,
a few houses below the one that housed the man who presided over
Attatie's offerings. She would return late at night and retire to bed.

As the months went by, Granny Kadi began receiving friends at
our house. Those who came while she was cooking would help her
debone fish, pound pepper, or cut potato leaves. After a while, they
would disappear into her bedroom for a few minutes before the visitor
would come out and leave.

Then one day, Granny from Boyle Street sent a message to my
mother that she was concerned about our house being used as an *omole*
bar, and Granny Kadi swore she consumed alcohol only on occasions
when she went out with friends, and that she never sold alcohol at our
house.

Boyle Street

It was not very long after the birth of the twins that I came home from school to find Mohammed stooped naked in the middle of the sitting room. I thought he was being sweated, except there was no old man in a kaftan, no cauldron, no blankets over his body. Instead, sweat was dripping down the whip marks covering his skin, and cane splinters covered the living room chairs and linoleum.

"They're te-te-telling stories, Ma. They're te-te-telling stories about me."

He was crying and swiping his bottom here and there on the slippery floor to dodge the cane. Attatie was sweating like a child preparing for the common entrance exams. Her unwrapped head looked like a fowl's nest.

She was still within what she called the tender stage of childbirth—those forty days during which she avoided the rigors of stepping out of the gate, and even washing her hair. But she had abandoned that caution now, in her effort to straighten up her only son. Her chest heaved with one exerted stroke after the other, each punctuated by Mohammed's deafening defense.

"They're lying, Ma. They're te-te-telling stories."

His face contorted into hard, bumpy shapes, and tough ropes swelled Attatie's own forehead.

"Where were you all day today?" she said.

"I didn't go-go anywhere," he cried. "I was at school a-a-all day, Ma. They're te-te-telling stories."

"Shut up! Attatie screamed. "All your teachers together cannot tell a lie on you."

Another stroke landed on his slippery back. He screamed another hasty denial, rubbing the sore spot. More tears mixed with sweat on the linoleum.

"They're ly-ly-lying, Ma. They're ly-ly-lying."

"Shut up!" Attatie's voice was hoarse.

She was wiping the sweat off her face with the edge of her cotton wrapper. I wished she would sit down. She looked as though she could faint at any minute.

"You're speaking too fast," she said. "Anyone who speaks that fast is a liar."

She reached for a bowl I had not noticed on the stool behind her. She splashed some of the water on Mohammed's body, as if to wash out the chips and uncover new landings for her cane. Mohammed screamed and held his hand over his head to intercept the cane. Another mark was added to his arm, followed with a succession of hits on his head, back, and legs.

"Someone go-go and call Granny for me!" he screamed, stealing looks toward the front and back doors. "She's killing me. My-my mother is killing me."

Sometimes, in the heat of caning one child, if a sibling happened to pass by, Attatie would shout, "Don't you have something to do! Don't you have a book to read!"

And if you were slow in providing your reason for being in that place at that moment, she would help you along with a stroke or two. At other times, she would say something like, Where were you when your sister or brother was breaking the tumbler? Or, *Why didn't you do something to stop your sister or brother from breaking the tumbler? How many times have I said you are all responsible for one another?*

And before you could come up with an excuse as to why you did not stop your sibling from breaking the tumbler, she would earmark you for half the number of strokes the wrongdoer was getting.

So when Mohammed called for someone to take a message to Granny, I hurried away to a veranda chair to make pretense of opening my book.

"Now pick up your uniform and go put on some clothes," I heard her say to Mohammed.

"I'm not coming back to-to this house for the res-rest of my life!" he screamed. "N-no one will ever, ever s-see me again."

I was about ten years old, and he was still my hero. But I couldn't help laughing at his struggle to sound firm, even as he ran away from Attatie, all the while pulling up his pants and cutting glances backward to make sure Attatie was not coming after him.

***

Whenever we visited Attatie's childhood home on Sackville Street, it didn't matter if it was Amie or Mohammed or Fatmata standing in front of Grandpa Karimu—he saw me first. He would rise from his hammock, his fragile arms outstretched in front of him as though to collect the wind.

"Mameh, Mameh, Mameh Bambakai."

He repeated my name so often, my mother had to explain that he always thinks of his late daughter after whom I was named, each time he saw me.

Attatie translated between us from Soso to Krio and back.

"He wants to know how you're doing."

With my head on Grandpa Karimu's chest, I would form wide grins and say, "Tell him I'm doing well."

One of the few fond memories Sackville Street relatives often repeated of Mohammed was him calling his mother *Attatie* when he couldn't say Aunty Amie, as his older cousins did. And everyone called my mother Attatie, after Mohammed. It was he who dominated at Boyle Street.

"My husband, what would you like me to cook for you today?"

Mohammed would grin and gloat and call for cassava leaves, and we would all have to eat cassava leaves. If we happened to visit on a day when okra soup or any other slippery sauce like crain-crain had already been decided on, Granny would dispatch her hand-and-foot girl to Bombay Street market for a fresh set of fish, pepper, onions, palm oil, and cassava leaves. Even Amie, who was named after Granny, did not receive a fraction of the attention Mohammed did.

"Are these your grandchildren?" a woman once asked.

"Yes. You know who this is?" Granny said, ignoring Amie, who was standing in front of her.

Even before the visitor attempted a name, she replied, "This is Mohammed. Momodu Wullay, my husband."

The woman dropped her chin and pulled Mohammed into a big embrace, kissing him, rubbing her hands over his head, as though in reunion with a long-departed god.

"This man whose name you carry," she said to Mohammed, "he was a good Muslim. He was the best amongst men. He never spoke a lie in his life."

Mohammed was beaming.

"You must show this man a lot of respect," the woman told Amie and me.

On the evening after Attatie had caned Mohammed, Aminata, Granny's hand-and-foot child, came to our house with a message. Papa was sitting on the veranda, smoking a cigarette, and Attatie was in the sitting room, feeding Hassana. It was clear to all of us that she had come about Mohammed, but poor Aminata had to squeeze herself inside of the space between two chairs and grip the arm of another before she could bring herself to greet Attatie.

"Good evening," Attatie replied, keeping her focus on the baby's feeding bottle.

Aminata fumbled with the edges of her wrapper. "I-I'm here, Ma, because Granny has sent me."

Attatie looked her up and down, and up again, before settling her gaze on Aminata's, toes which were now buried into the linoleum.

"Granny sent me to ask…"

"What did Granny send you to ask?"

Aminata played with the edge of her wrapper again, before she lowered her voice.

"She wants to know, Ma…"

"What does Granny want to know?"

"Mohammed came to Boyle Street this afternoon, ma."

"He was supposed to be here with his books!" Attatie snapped.

"He said you caned him, ma."

"Tell your granny that Mohammed has been missing school for days."

Aminata gasped.

"He didn't tell that to Granny, ma. He said he was beaten because the teacher told lies on him."

Aminata's steps were lighter when she left, but she returned the following morning as we were getting ready for school, with orders from Granny to collect Mohammed's school uniform.

"Go and get the uniform yourselves," Attatie replied, obviously including Granny in the *selves*.

"Yes, ma." Aminata went into the bedroom, where I helped her collect Mohammed's gray khaki trousers and white shirt.

We didn't see Mohammed for almost a week, until he tagged behind Papa one evening. Attatie gave them both her back. Papa asked him to wait in the living room. He went into their bedroom and returned with a cane. Mohammed exploded. None of his outbursts, however, appeared to reach Papa's ears. The cane marks he showed from Attatie's beatings, the pain on his legs from stooping on the floor, all were well-deserved, according to Papa.

"I'm going to give you twelve strokes so that you will think twice before you decide, next time, to skip school."

I had missed him in the last few days he wasn't home. I felt sorry for him going through so much beating, even for missing school.

Papa started with a lecture. "Before you become a dropout and a wrangler, roaming about in the streets—for that is what you are destined to become without an education—I will make sure there is enough pain on your back to match the pain you put your mother and I through."

It was always easier to intervene when Papa was speaking, than with Attatie. I knew I could speak on Mohammed's behalf. He was still my hero. But first, I watched Attatie. Her gaze was still outside the door. I kept my focus on her as I tiptoed over to Papa.

"Give him six," I pleaded.

Mohammed was now prostrate on the floor, still sobbing, lamenting how much his teachers hated him, how they tell lies on him, and what he was going to do to each one of them.

Papa landed the first stroke on his bare back. "I don't go to work to put food on the table for a wrangler."

He accompanied each stroke with a justification, until he reached six. That's when I tugged on the edge of his trousers.

"You're lucky your sister has begged for you."

I stole a glance to make sure Attatie had not heard what Papa just said. I knew the possible consequences for me.

Mohammed finally got off the ground and stormed out of the room, threatening to kill each and every one of the teachers at his school.

Pray Day

For adults, Eid-ul-Fitri was a day of prayer and release from the ascetic pressures of Ramadan month. You wore new clothes, new shoes, plenty of jewelry. You expressed appreciation to Allah for having shown you yet another year of Eid, and you asked that you see many more Eids in good health. For us children, Prayday was a time to parade the streets and show off the new clothes and shoes we had earned after a year of good behavior.

It is the anticipation in the days before Prayday that stays with me the most.

"Go wash your feet, everybody, and change your clothes. We're going to Bata Shoe Store."

I would fight with Amie for the water pan and the rush to get dressed for the once-a-year taxi ride with Papa for new shoes.

A week or two before Prayday, I would sit on the linoleum with my sisters to brainstorm with Attatie on how we can stand out on Prayday. One year, we were dressed like little Yoruba women. We wore cropped tops with long loose sleeves, and knee-high wrappers, together with large headties. Another year, we were little Indians, with pink saris, flat slippers, and little pink umbrellas. Yet another year, we were little Mandinga women, with cobalt blue tie-dye *fente* gowns and long wrappers.

The year we were going to be little Christian women, Granny got involved. The rumors were that one of my cousin's, Rugie, Aunty Fatmata's daughter of Papa's half-sister, had not gone to Eid prayers the previous year because she had nothing to wear. But Aunty Fatmata said Rugie had not gone to prayers because she spilled a gallon of palm oil on the dirt ground. That was the thing about Prayday—one false move during those last few days of Ramadan, and you do not get to show off your new clothes.

Anyway, Attatie took the nothing-to-wear side of the story and bought enough fabric for Rugie, and for good measure, Rugie's younger sister, to dress as little Christian girls on Prayday. Then word got out about Attatie's plan to include Aunty Fatmata's children in our Prayday fashion, and Aunty Mariama's three daughters, too, ended up in the Christian-girl fashion.

Of course, Boyle Street had to be included. There was a spiky little girl who lived in a bungalow adjacent to Granny's house. She spent all day at Granny's yard, and sometimes even spent the night there. She was included. Also included was the daughter of Granny's stepson, a girl whose mother left her with Granny when she was not yet five years old, to go on a business trip in the provinces. She returned only once or twice a year, with gifts of fruits and pennies for her daughter.

So it was like carnival at our house, when the girls from Boyle Street, Jenkins Street, and Cardew Street came to be measured for their dresses. We giggled and exchanged bold Prayday resolutions like, "I'm going to wake up on Prayday when it's still dark outside," and designating Grandpa Fabilo as the first adult to visit after Eid prayers.

Attatie, meanwhile, busied herself turning every girl around, one at a time, to lay her tape measure on a shoulder-to-elbow, the round of a burst, and the length from a shoulder to the indent below the knee cap. A few days later, she cut ten little shapes out of the pastel blue crepe before taking them to an embroiderer who decorated the neck, arms, and hemline with shimmering silver thread.

The dresses were ready a few days before Prayday, and Abassy delivered parcels to Jenkins Street, Cardew Street, and Boyle Street. Abassy returned with a question from Granny.

"Where's Marie Swarray's dress?

"Who is Marie Swarray?" Attatie asked Abassy.

I explained that Marie Swarray was a granddaughter of one of Granny's relatives who had recently come to live with her.

Attatie replied, "Who is Marie Swarray to me?" Thick ropes formed on her neck. "Tell Granny there's no more embroidery thread left. I bought the last roll from the store."

It was a few days before Prayday, and of course items were scarce in stores, so I thought my mother's response would satisfy Granny. But the next day, the eve before Prayday, Aminata came and stammered a follow-up message from Granny.

"Attatie af-af-ternoon me."

"Bo, are say, what do you want?" Attatie snapped. "This is Eid-ul-fitri eve. I have a lot to do."

"Granny, said, said, ma." Aminata was not a stammerer, but stuck between Attatie and Granny, the poor girl was seldom able to speak.

"What did your Granny say this time? Hurry up and speak. I have things to do."

"Well, ma. Granny said, said, ma. She, she, said ma, that if-if," Aminata glanced furtively around her as though expecting to be pounced up after she delivers her message. "If-if you don't. She said ma, if-if you don't get Marie Swarray a dress ma."

"If I don't get Marie Swarray a dress, what will your Granny do to me? Will she undo my wrapper and flog me?"

"No, no, ma." Aminata rushed to answer. "She said, said, ma, that your children, ma, will-will not go-go to prayers, ma."

"The audacity of your grandmother," Attatie said to me after Aminata had managed to disappear. "Who is Marie Swarray to me?" she kept repeating.

I did not respond. I did not understand how Granny could stop us from going to Eid prayers if Attatie and Papa said we could.

***

Prayday was the one day of the year when educated Muslims in Freetown were able to get away with not dressing like Westerners. All other times, you wore a dress or a skirt and straightened and curled your hair. Otherwise, you were scorned, on the streets and in the workplace, in spite of your education, for looking *uncivilized*. Maybe it was a respite, out of sympathy, for Muslims having endured thirty days of fasting. Or maybe it was relief from thirty days of usurping street sidewalks for evening prayers, and the end of long and frosty spittle on street paths. Whatever it was, Christians got up early on Prayday to stand on sidewalks or on their windows and verandas to root for us on our way to prayers. They would say, "Lovely dress," "Don't forget to pray for me," and "That is exactly the dress I want to wear on Christmas Day."

Ma Abel would be beside herself with contrived excitement.

"My, who are those beautiful girls? Think I can borrow those dresses for Christmas Day?"

I nodded agreement, pridefully twisting my little frame this way and that. The Penninas and the Porters came onto their windows before long, and the Ashcrofts lined up on their veranda.

"My, my, what beautiful girls! What beautiful dresses. What beautiful hairdo. Is that really Mameh? Is that Amie? Let me take another look."

I would pat what was left of my stretched and curled hair after the night's humidity had returned most of it to its coarse state, leaving only a few curled tips and wide gaps all over my head.

"Mameh's going to let me wear her dress, with the shoes and socks, for Christmas," Ma Abel would boast, to which Mammy Penina would feign envy and say, "Oh, how very, very lucky you are, Mabel," and resolved to borrow our handbags and umbrellas instead.

Even Miss Fenella stood behind her father on the second floor of their house and grinned and asked if she could borrow something or other we were wearing.

Not to be outdone, Mr. Pinkney and his sister came onto the empty lot in front of our house. Mr. Pinkney, in khaki shorts and a rumpled shirt he always seemed to have quickly thrown on, would stand legs apart, hands folded over his stomach bulge.

"I'm an utterly confused man this morning," he would say, "seeing so many beautiful girls all at once."

Of course, the many beautiful girls were only Amie and me, but his sister would nod profusely.

Mohammed did not get as many compliments. He was required to follow what Papa said was the family custom from his own father and wear one of Papa's old Prayday gowns that had been fitted for him, with a fez that covered half his forehead like he was wearing a deep pot. Mr. Pinkney would bow when Papa stepped onto the veranda decked from head to toe in his departed father's best Prayday clothes—dark-colored kaftan with long sleeves, chest and neckline embroidered with silk thread. The tassel on his fez cap was usually the color of his umbrella.

Mr. Pinkney would bow a good morning, bow to his sister's own good morning, and even to Papa's response.

Ma Abel would spread out her arms to tell the neighborhood, "If his father were missing, he could go find him dressed like that."

Papa would respond by sucking hard on his cigarette and turning around to shout to Attatie that we might miss the prayers if she did not hurry up.

Attatie was still giving final instructions to the houseboy about the jollof rice and other delicacies to be consumed later. She always made the last appearance. Even as she busied herself during the final weeks of Ramadan, with our dresses and the final series of rice pap and beans cake she distributed to friends and relatives, she did not shrink the focus on herself. Her gown, her shoes and jewelry, head tie and handbag, she would say, are to be, for a long time after Prayday day, the subject of conversation amongst all who had seen me on Prayday.

From the second week of Ramadan, she began going around stores with a strip from the fabric already in the seamstress's hand. She had to make sure she got the right color shoes to match her gown. Then she sent Papa to the goldsmith shop with the pattern of jewelry she wanted to wear on Prayday. If the pattern that arrived did not suit her fancy, then, amidst derisive whispers about the work that Papa's uncles did, she raided her deceased grandmother's jewelry box. One morning, while wearing her grandmother's jewelry, she stepped onto the veranda in a low neck Yoruba top and wrapper, accessorized with gold earrings that covered the length of her earlob, a matching necklace, and a head tie twice the size of her head. Her shawl and umbrella had matching gold sequins, matching the gold beads that decorated the wrists of her white gloves.

Mr. Pinkney folded his hands behind his back and took a bow. Attatie's lips expanded only so far, one eyelid dropping as she panned her head and waved a gloved hand, first to Ma Abel, then to Mammy Porter and to Mammy Penina, and down to Mr. Pinkney and his sister, to end, most charitably, with the Ashcrofts on their veranda.

***

The cars knew better than to appear on Goree Street on Prayday morning. The children would have put up a fight. They held hands to form a crooked line that took up the breadth of the street, their new rubber slippers flipping and flopping with the jollity of their steps. One or two of the younger ones straddled behind, clutching reed mats under their armpits.

The boys wore long pants under short kaftans. Some of the pants were rolled up so many times, they formed puffy cuffs around the ankles. Unlike their mismatched clothing of regular days, the girls' hip-length blouses matched their wrappers. In some cases, oversized blouses drooped over a shoulder or two, and a girl here and there struggled with an oversized head tie.

Some of the slippers were uncomfortably oversized, but no one was barefoot, and there were no rips in any of the clothes. The snotty noses and soiled faces were wiped clean. You almost couldn't recognize the children from the bottom of Goree Street.

I reached our gate, taking care not to step on red dirt or dog or fowl poop. I was standing in front of the street gutter when their parade came by with their appearances and noisy chatter overwhelming even Mr. Pinkney, who seemed ready to salute them.

The Conteh girls followed, together with the older women.

"Asalamualaikum," one of the women called out to my parents.

She was wearing the same blue rococo lace fabric as the girls.

"Wa alaikum salam," Papa and Attatie replied.

"May Allah allow us to see next year's Eid," Attatie said.

"Inshallah," the women chorused.

Amie and I were about to step over the gutter to join the Conteh girls, when Attatie put a hand in front of me to wait. She had seen Mr. and Mrs. Kallay.

Mr. Kallay had on a blue flowing gown and matching fez. Mrs. Kallay wore a bottle-green lace gown with more holes than fabric.

"Asalamualaikum," said the husband.

"Wa alaikum salam," Papa replied.

"Let us thank Allah for the privilege of another Eid in good health," Attatie said to Mrs. Kallay.

"Alhamdudilai, said Mrs. Kallay. "Let us pray we can assemble like this again next year."

"Inshallah." Attatie motioned for us to walk with them.

The new sun was boldest at the Goree Street intersection of Bombay Street. A breeze distributed topaz and other flowery incenses. The joyful Eid Takbir had begun. Papa's Uncles and cousins from Boyle Street, the men and women from Cardew Street and Lower Bombay Street, Aunty Memuna and Uncle Muctarr from Elba Street were all present. Parents held hands with children to sing the *takbir*. Uncle Sumaila complimented my jewelry and thanked me for choosing his gifts over that of Papa's uncles. Grandpa Osman asked how many days I had fasted and put the equivalent in shillings in my hand.

The first girl I saw in a cobalt-blue embroidered dress was beaming with the happiness of a well-fed toddler. She was skipping between the crowds, grinning and peeping into each little passageway that opened as the adults moved with the rhythm of the Takbir.

"Marie Swarray!" I called out in surprise.

Her eyes dilated. Her shawl was not brand-new. It was one that Granny used for Friday prayers, but her eyes danced disco in their sockets as she took in my dress, the embroideries on the neck, the arms, the hemline, then brushed down her own dress, in disbelief that it was the same as mine.

***

At Kissy Road, the Clock Tower and Fullah Town group joined our procession. It wasn't just Christians that lined up the streets now. There were those people without the means to dress up for Prayday, and those who did not confine their call on ancestors and wooden gods only to trying times. Those whom Christians and Muslims agree are pagans. They joined the Christians to watch, maybe admire us display abundant praise upon one entity. And they all beseeched us, customarily, to remember them in our prayers.

The Fullah Town people said greetings like *Eku Audun*, and other Yoruba tongues. Attatie exchanged *Eku Awdun* with them, with more zest than she had done with the Kallay's "Asalamualaikum."

She had grown up amongst the Fullah Town people, and had picked up their Yorobanized Islam, as well as their penchant for bold actions. Everyone now repeated,

"*Eku Awdun! Eku Awdun!*" Everyone agreed that much thanks was due to Allah, and that another Eid in good health was most desirable, *insh'Allah*.

When we reached the Savage Squire junction; the procession swelled, the *Takbir* spirited, the

Eku Awduns multiplied. Another Yorobanized group, the Fourah Bay procession, emerged from the depths of side streets, up and down the Squire, with agile steps and bold-smelling perfumes. They talked and sang in high pitches, especially the women, who did more talking than singing.

"Indeed, it pays to marry a goldsmith's son, doesn't it?" joked a tall, high-chested woman in a lace gown and silver necklace.

Before Attatie could respond, another woman said, "Her husband's uncles are in business just to make her beautiful jewelry."

"But look at the quality of that lace," Attatie said to the high-chested woman, "compared to the old thing I saw your husband wearing."

"Does that surprise you?" The woman shot back. "Mister Cole has to wear an old rag so I can look like this."

Every woman within earshot threw her head back and laughed. And so did the children around them.

I had an experience from one of the first Eid prayers I can remember. I was about four or five years old. I had a thin sequined shawl which would not stay put over my head tie. I had managed to keep it on while we were all seated on the prayer rug, but as soon as we got up to start the prayers, the shawl slid down my back. I spent minutes first trying to stop its slide, and then trying to bring the shawl over my head and make it stay there. By the time I felt it secured enough on my head so that I could bend down in prayer like everyone else, I noticed everyone else was already sitting. My mother was stretching out her legs, making herself comfortable on the mat over the graveled ground. The prayers, which I had anticipated for weeks, for which I had put up good behavior for weeks, had lasted the time it took to adjust my shawl. I cried all the way home. To make things worse, word got around to my cousins that I did not actually attend prayers that Eid. From that day, I learned that as soon as we reached the Kissy Road cemetery and Cline Town roundabout, I had to begin making sure my shawl was in place over my head and covering my jaws and chin.

The Cline Town roundabout was where sons went with their fathers, and daughters with their mothers. The field was already swollen with worshippers when we entered, the resonance of "Eid Takbir" replacing the chants of the usual football crowd.

Papa's Uncles

apa's sisters and uncles were visiting, but no one had died, and there was no baby to name. Instead, Grandpa Osman was assigning seats as though they were meeting for a group session. "You, Borbor," he called to his cousin in a black beret. "Drag your chair close to mine."

Grandpa Osman was standing in front of the armchair he had commandeered for himself, the one in the middle of the row of four or five chairs. There was a side stool next to the chair. He put his hand under the stool to make sure it was secure.

"Abdul, you sit here by the door," he told his older brother.

Grandpa Abdul had a voice as soft as his babyface, and a few strands of gray hair. He made a joke about younger brothers and commanding spirits, but Grandpa Osman, the Djeliba of the family, went ahead assigning seats to his two other older brothers. One brother had a seat next to the window, and the other close to the sheet rock that separated our living and dining rooms.

Except for the chair next to the bedroom door on which Attatie sat, every other one in the house was now occupied. Aunty Fatmata brought in a backyard bench she shared with her sister, and Papa brought himself a chair from the dining room. I had already secured a spot on the floor against the sheet rock.

"Does anyone know how much I paid for bread this morning?" Grandpa Osman stretched his legs out.

"But your family is not even as large as mine," Grandpa Abdul replied. "Think of what I spend on food these days."

Everyone nodded, and Grandpa Borbor ripped off his beret and said the price of a cup of rice had almost doubled in a month.

Papa said, "Even the children who come to eat our food offerings have increased in age."

And Attatie said that their numbers had gone up, too.

"Not like the days when you needed to coax some of them to come and help make your prayers a success," she said.

"Let us pray," Grandpa Osman said, after the small talk, then continued to *Al-Fatiah*."

Attatie shouted her son's name, and Mohammed joined the gathering with a frown that was becoming him those days. He wanted nothing to do with adults, especially Papa and Attatie, and often talked about running away to Ethiopia, where his real relatives lived. His friends all called him Selassie. He had conjectured that Sillah was short for Selassie. In Ethiopia, he would sit next to Haile Selassie and escape the company of the base beings to which he was now shackled.

"Sit on the floor in front of me so our eyes can meet," Grandpa Osman said.

Mohammed took his time following the orders, amassing more frown lines as he darted tentative looks at Attatie.

"If you don't put your behind on the floor right now…"

He succumbed quickly.

Everyone in the congregation had questions for Mohammed.

"Where did you go? Why in Allah's great creation would your teacher tell lies on you? Don't you know the man whose name you carry? Don't you know your importance to this family?"

To which Mohammed said, "I-I didn't go anywhere, sir. I-I was in school all-all the time, Ma."

And Grandpa Osman, every now and then, reminded him of the crowds he might join in hell if he didn't mind his denials.

There was a brief silence.

Then Aunty Mariama said, "You're the only male child in the family. You need to pull yourself together."

Attatie brought the edge of her wrapper to her eyes. She knew that Mohammed on the floor, together with his barrage of lies, was worth more than a hundred of those girls she had born.

"Soon, you're going to bear the responsibility for all four of your sisters," Aunty Mariama continued.

"That's going to take a man." Granpa Borbor shook a wrinkled fist.

"It is to your house they will go when their husbands beat them," Aunty Fatmata said.

To this, Mohammed threw me a look I understood well. If I didn't look sharp, he wouldn't come to my aide when I'm being beaten by my husband.

I was not unfamiliar with wife beating. Ma Abel once had a tenant whose cries we often heard behind the closed doors when her husband beat her. She would emerge from their one-room apartment the next day and go about her chores as though nothing had happened. But I had never saw or heard of the educated woman I was going to become—women like Mrs. Jarrett and Miss Fenella—being beaten by their husbands.

Grandpa Osman followed Aunty Fatmata's point by alluding to a story I grew up hearing from Granny.

"We pray that Allah give your sisters to men like your grandfather," he said. "He was a good man who only beat my sister when she deserved it."

Granny had explained one of those beatings she had received from her thirty-year-old husband.

"I went to my girlfriend's house to get my hair braided. I was only about thirteen or fourteen years old, and we enjoyed each other's company so much, I returned home too late to prepare my husband's meal on time. He had me lie on the floor for twelve strokes."

It was one of Granny's most sober memories of her late husband.

"That was the only time I gave my husband cause," she said.

Sister Mariama said with pride, that her own husband never laid hands on her, mainly because of Papa's manly uprightness.

Grandpa Borbor, returning his black beret to a bald head, associated part of what he called his *broken mouth*, to fighting with *that vagabond* to whom his own sister was once married.

"You might find yourself with the responsibility of fighting with four men like that," he told Mohammed, to which everyone prayed that Allah protects Mohammed from such horrific associations.

But why, in Allah's good name, does Mohammed not follow his namesake's example, or even his father's? A man raised by a single mother. How efficiently he ran errands as a little boy. How much praise the neighbors hurled at him. From where did Mohammed's character come? The questions were thrown here and here.

"Look at your mother," said Grandpa Osman. "A young child who lost her mother before she was even conscious of such a thing as a mother. Raised by grandparents. Neighbors never complained about her. No one said anything loose about her comportment. Look how well she turned out. Good enough for your father to marry. Look at their beautiful children. Turn around," he told Mohammed. "Look at your beautiful sisters."

I was the only sister present, but Djelibas don't have to be exact.

"I say, turn around and look at them. What more can a man want? What good man wouldn't want to marry your sisters?"

Mohammed did not turn around. Instead, he clamped his eyelids together, pursed his lips and pouted something under his breath. He was growing disgusted with every word, his hands hanging over the knees now, like a bored gorilla. This is a group he'd be well rid of in Ethiopia.

I, on the other hand, had my brains on fire trying to understand my parents, especially Papa. I had gotten used to Papa using me as an example for Mohammed to follow.

"Look at Mameh," he would say. "She's not even the child you called. There is one other child between the two of you. And a girl, for that matter. Look how well she does at school."

If Papa had any hopes still sitting on Mohammed, he was not doing much to show it. With Amie's speech defect, little by little, he was edging toward me, pushing me to do well in school, and promising to send me to England. Attatie, too, had encouraged, if not fostered, my dreams of going to England and coming back like Mrs. Jarrett, and even Miss Fenella, who didn't even have a husband. Soon, I began to see Mohammed less as a fun-loving older brother, and more as an equal.

That night, I struggled to answer the questions: Why didn't Papa speak up? Why didn't he talk about my school performance? Why didn't he repeat the examples he always urged Mohammed to copy from me, to his uncles?

***

The second time Papa's uncles and sisters came was a few days after a piece of meat had been missing from my rice. It was a year after Amie had missed a class, and we were going to sit the Common Entrance exams together. I had grown as tall as she—only heavier. We often dressed alike from head to toe, and people would ask if we were twins. Attatie sometimes treated us as twins. "You see, this piece is the same size as that piece, so no one is getting more than the other."

If she cooked chicken, each person got a leg the same size. Amie and I compared everything, from panties to earrings to pencil sharpeners. We would put two pieces of meat side by side, turn each one around, and weigh them in our hands so the person with the perceived larger piece could boast.

But we had to eat from the same bowl, with the cassava leaves or whatever the sauce, on top of the rice.

"It is sisterly," Attatie said. "And it will help you stay together when you are adults."

Mohammed had his own bowl, with his sauce on top of his rice mound. Only Papa's rice and sauce were placed in separate bowls.

I opened our bowl one day and noticed only one piece from the beef stew on top of the rice, next to a large dent where the other piece had been. Amie and I had arrived home together, so I knew she had not yet been to the dining room. I picked up the bowl of rice and went to confront Mohammed in the bedroom.

"I didn't take it," he said.

"Yes, you did!" I shouted.

He waved a dismissive hand, filled his chest with air, and stammered orders for me to leave the room.

I took the bowl of rice to Attatie on the veranda. She got up from her sewing machine and came to the dining room, took a piece of beef from Papa's sauce bowl to replace the stolen piece, then began heading way back, all without saying a word.

I was pleased to have my piece of beef back, but Mohammed was getting away with it. This is something for which I would have received serious lectures, if not the cane. I was at an age where I had realized he was able to identify the make and color of cars on Goree Street, only because of the holes in the veranda zinc.

At the same time, my anger was swelling, Attatie was returning to the veranda, and Mohammed was emerging from the bedroom wearing a look that said, *I can do whatever I want. no one will ask me questions.*

It tore me up inside. I had just come home from school; I was tired, and I was hungry. I was without patience, without fear. I completely dismissed my mother's presence.

"You dog child!" I shouted and sucked hard on my teeth.

I cannot say how quickly Attatie turned around. All I can do is describe the heat on my ears, like a furnace had opened up around its lobe, against the cold numbness my mother's hand left on my jaw.

"In this house, you don't talk to your older brother like that."

Her words came out as if from a spitfire. "Even if he's not older, he's a man, and you're a woman."

During the meeting called to help put me in my place, I stood in the center of the room, facing my granduncles.

"You've been talking to your brother in ways a sister does not talk to her older brother," said Grandpa Osman.

I had my hands behind my back, gaze to the ground.

"Do not look down on your brother because of what he is today," Grandpa Osman continued. "He's a man. Boys do not spoil, only girls do."

"Indeed, boys do not get pregnant, whereas girls do," another said.

"Boys can change miraculously," said another. "But girls, once spoiled, are spoiled for good," said another.

"Mohammed may be skipping school," Grandpa said, "even failing his exams today, but he may also, one day, become a cabinet minister and ride in a Mercedes Benz. A girl doesn't have much chance of that."

"Indeed, once spoiled, a girl is spoiled for good."

"When your husband doesn't give you enough chop money," Grandpa Osman continued, "it is to your brother that you will go to supplement the home and make your husband happy."

"You will be proud, then, to say he is your older brother. And then, where will..."

The words ceased making way into my ears. The room was already spinning, with my head bouncing against its panels. I landed in a world where I talked back to adults. I asked them how is it that when Attatie and Papa went out, they secured their bedroom key with me.

How come Papa always asked Mohammed to follow my example, and not the other way around. Yet, when we grow up, it was Mohammed who will be riding the Mercedes Benz, and I the battered wife with not enough money to feed my children?

Mortal Man

My mother had an interesting read on what she called *mortal man*. A read she'd learned from one of the Freetown women she emulated. Sissy Ramatu was older than my mother, and wife of Mr. Wurie, a politician who lived in a large brick house opposite that of Grandpa Fabilo.

After Mr. Conteh left, Attatie pointed to his empty apartment and shook her head.

"Mortal man! He stayed in a big place like this and paid almost nothing in rent, and all he repaid us with is a curse on my only son."

The laborers who carried the large bags into the storage room expected more money than she was willing to give.

"Mortal Man!" she would say. "They always want more than they deserve."

When Granny insisted on the Prayday dress for Marie Swarray, my mother cried, "Mortal man! I bought Prayday cloths for all her grandchildren, out of my own pocket. And instead of thanking me, she insists on one more for her relative." After Papa paid for Marie Swarray's dress, she said, "Mortal man. He didn't pay for his own daughters' dresses."

In addition to sewing, teaching her apprentices, and selling rice, Attatie was now attending political meetings. When clients came for their dresses, she pitched not only the rice you could get only from Aminata Sillah, but also the APC Opposition Party. She had new friends she called comrades. She attended weddings, funerals, 40th Day ceremonies, christenings of comrade families.

One time, she returned from a political rally in the up-country with a loaded suitcase and travel bag. She had brought the usual food from the provinces: gari, oranges, newly harvested rice and corn, fried fish with cassava bread. Amie and I sat on the linoleum, watching her unpack.

"Remember what I told you Sissy Ramatu always says about mortal man?" She poked her lips out—one of her expressions of doom. "A mortal man is a mere mortal. Even if he's blind."

She was holding the cement paper already soaked in palm kernel oil from the fried fish, layers of cassava bread piled in her other hand. It was one of my favorite treats from Waterloo, and I was impatient to get to it.

"Do you know what the Freetown blind said when we asked the up-country blind to lead them in the party song?"

"Which song?" I said.

She had been coming home just before Maghrib sunset, with new party songs, together with stories about her comrades—men and women whose names we usually heard on the radio. There was Comrade S.I. Koroma, the deputy head of the Opposition; Comrade Nancy Steele, who led the women's wing.

My mother told us a gripping story once, of how Comrade Olamatu Cole stood up to a soldier with a gun. She made us sing party songs. We held up our hands and joined our thumbs and index finger to form a zero, then moving our heads from side to side, we sang, "*APC subamukuramo, karamu kakuma, ikaramukakuma, ikaramukakuma.* It was the first time she encouraged us to utter any words in a language other than Krio or English.

"What did the Freetown blind say?" Attatie replied.

Amie was already chuckling at the term *Freetown blind.*

"They said they're from the city." Attatie pushed her lips out even further. "That they would not be led in a song by the up-country blind."

"What did they do in the end?" I said.

"Oh, we stood our ground. We told them we were in up-country, so the up-country blind should lead the song." She took a pinch of the cassava bread. "This is what you must always remember about mortal man: everybody wants to be above somebody."

Pools and Politics

G randpa Borbor and Uncle Sumaila used to come to our house on Saturday evenings to play football pools with Papa. They would hold their pens and coupons in front of them like pupils in a classroom, and glue their ears to the raspy shortwave transmission. Liverpool 1, Manchester 2. Leicester 3, Watford 2. The smallest amount of noise was promptly shooed, as they marked frantic X's on the coupons' narrow grids. Papa's friends, Mr. Howard and Mr. Finney, would join them, together with the neighbor, Mr. Tommy. When the general election campaigns started, the pools hours began extending into the night.

Granny Kadi prepared fried plantains or potatoes, and fried fish. I would help serve the snacks, then sit on my slab until someone called for water, or a towel, or for an ashtray to be emptied.

After the pools had been marked and the radio turned off, the high-pitched grievances began.

"The SLPP is a *Mende-man* party," said Uncle Borbor. "Only the prime minister's own tribe gets cabinet positions and good jobs." He would remove his beret and declare himself ready to lose more teeth in the fight for the opposition party.

Uncle Sumaila usually said the least, only agreeing with talk about the times getting too hard.

Mr. Finney, a short man with piercing eyes, a churchgoing creole and Papa's colleague, would complain about not enough creoles in the prime minister's cabinet.

Mr. Howard, a hefty creole, was one of those children from well-to-do families who were sent to England in the days when Sierra Leoneans believed Europe magically transformed a problem child into a doctor or a lawyer. He had returned only after his father's death, to collect rent from the old man's three-story property in front of which he sat all day long, watching people go about their businesses. In the evening, he came to our house to partake in Papa's dinner.

When Mr. Finney spoke, Mr. Howard added *Uh-huhs*, and, "That's right," but contributed little to the grievances.

Mr. Tommy was born Soso but raised by a creole family. He usually said things like, "We need to speak up about that," and, "The creoles will never put up with that."

One of Attatie's uncles from Sackville Street, Grandpa Morlai, himself an APC candidate for East II constituency, sometimes joined the gathering. He would speak about tribal unity, and pronounced the opposition leader, Siaka Stevens, who he said was a Limba, the only man able to accomplish that goal.

Those were eye-opening times for me. Other than my parents' tribe, the Sosos and Mandingas, and the creoles, who were my Christian teachers and school friends, I was unfamiliar with other groups. I was eleven years old and about to sit for the Common Entrance Examination. Nothing in my years of schooling had acquainted me with the character of the tribes of the country in which I was growing up.

I guarded my spot on the wood slab over the window and listened and learned, until the gatherings halted after Attatie was arrested.

The Women's Wing Rally

We were not yet settled. Our loud conversations from lunch break continued above the banging of desk covers as we searched for the right books for English. Mrs. Longstretch sat on her table and persisted above the din, pausing after every other word to wipe her short, bumpy face with a broad white handkerchief. The noise stopped only when Mrs. Kissling hurried into the classroom with her long stick. It was one of those few times when the stick was merely perfunctory—not carried for redress. She went straight to Mrs. Longstretch's table and whispered something in her ear. Mrs. Longstretch folded her lips and moved to my desk.

"Someone is here to take you home." Her voice was grave. "Pack up your bag and follow me."

Mariama Conteh was standing at the classroom door, holding Amie's hand.

"Your father has sent me to take you home right away." She looked like green sorrel.

Amie and I exchange frightened looks. Neither said a word. Neither did Mariama Conteh. She was one of Granny's teenage nieces now staying with her, and someone with whom we usually enjoyed older-cousin company. But on that afternoon, she simply held our hands as we left the school compound.

There were plenty of questions I could have asked, but I was probably afraid of the answer. Had my mother died? Also, I was afraid that maybe, by asking questions, I would be forgetting the bitter taste of kola nut juice Granny had squeezed onto my tongue.

Kissy Road was congested with convoys of army trucks and soldiers pointing gun barrels indiscriminately. I squeezed myself against the smell of firewood smoke and raw onion on Mariama Conteh's lap. It was obvious she had been pulled out of the kitchen to come and get us.

Neither Attatie nor Papa were home. Our living room fell into confused silence with our presence. The women of Sackville Street and Boyle Street began fussing over Amie and me.

"You want something to eat?"

"Look, Granny Kadi made some sweet cassava leaves."

"No, let them eat the biscuits first.

"There's Vimto, too. "

"Let me help you take off your uniform."

"What beautiful panties?"

I sat in silence next to Granny. The Vimto drink, sweet as it had been mixed, could have been mere water helping the biscuit down my throat.

Suddenly, the biscuit jammed my throat. I was jolted by the horn of a car and the sound of halting engine. I bounced up.

"Sit down." Granny tried to put a hand in front of me.

Too late. I was already on the veranda. Grandpa Morlai's banana-yellow Benz was parked in front of our gate. His bald head preceded the rest of his body out of the car. He glanced at the veranda with an uneasy expression.

Everybody, except Granny, had followed me to the veranda, and they all scrambled to put their wide hips in front of my face. I fought back, piercing my head into every narrow slit between an adult hip. I saw Papa get out of the car, looking as if he had not slept in days. Uncle Sumaila came out looking equally crushed.

It was after an eternity, between alternatively forcing my head into an opening between two hips, and stooping down between two legs, that I noticed the bottom edges of one of Attatie's wrappers—the one she was wearing that morning as she was getting ready to attend an APC Party rally. Her feet touched the tarred street like a feather on cotton wool. Papa and Grandpa Morlai reached for her arms and helped her out of the car.

Two large white plasters covered an eye, and her lips looked like large, motionless centipedes. As she toddled closer to the veranda steps, my first thought, as an eleven year old, was to disown this dis-

abled person. Her husband held one hand and directed one step, her
uncle the other. Even as they tried to move her forward, her body
remained as still as the patch on her eye, quiet as an animal wounded
into submission.

She looked around the house with anxiousness and trembled a
piece of white cloth over her lips. The house reeked of hospital smell.
Her gaze stopped at Amie, then me. Our eyes met. I dropped mine. I
didn't want Granny seeing my mother that way. I didn't want anyone
seeing my mother that way. That was the reason I broke down and
yielded to the fitful tears I let cover my face. The women gathered
around me, wiping my tears and hushing me. My mother remained on
the seat she had taken, powerless.

"Let's make a *dou'a*," Grandpa Morlai said. "Let us thank Allah for
not making our burden heavier. Let us thank Him for bringing home
our daughter, our wife, our sister, and our mother. Let us pray for our
country. Let us pray for the APC Party. Let us pray for the soldiers who
laid hands on our daughters. Let us pray for peace in our country." He
recited Al-Fatiah.

Everyone buzzed, "Ameen."

***

A few weeks later, when Attatie was still convalescing, a delegation
of Papa's uncles from Boyle Street held a meeting in our parlor. They
had invited a delegation from Sackville Street. Boyle Street advised
Sackville Street that its daughter must wash her hands off all political
activities. No more party meetings. No more political rallies. Papa's
work often takes him to the provinces. The children are too small yet.
For a woman, the husband, the children, the home should come first.

Latrine Yard Fight

When my breasts began to swell, Attatie said, "I don't want offers of marriage coming for you."

I felt guilty about the protruding bulge, so I squinted as she hammered it back with a wooden rice spoon.

Since I was a baby, Granny had begun stringing together on thick black thread, rows of tiny beads of red, green, blue, and encircling it around my waist. She said it showed I was a woman. Attatie said waist beads were for country girls. My sisters as well as my cousins at Granny's house all wore waist beeds, so I didn't take them off. The thread weakened, though, with daily baths, and the beads fell apart after a while. Granny would make a fresh set each time, with more rows as I grew older.

Later, when my periods came, Attatie replaced the beads with a thick leather band brought by an old man "all the way from the remotest village in the provinces," she said. "You will die if you allow any man to get close enough to touch it."

When, in a moment of rage, I challenged Annie Brown to "meet me behind the school latrine," it wasn't long before I was ready to eat my words with the worst prepared cornmeal from the school kitchen. I was thinking more about the leather around my waist than about my opponent as I made my way to the back of the latrine, surrounded by Fredericka, Barbara, Joy, and a few other girls cheerleading my corner. I was hoping Annie would think of how she would explain a torn uniform to her grandmother and change her mind about the fight. I had never gotten into a fistfight before, but I had helped cheerlead plenty.

Maybe I could feign a sudden headache. But calling off a fight I had initiated would have serious consequences not only for my own reputation, but for the girls in my corner. I could postpone the fight for Monday, when I could come to school without the waist cord. But what reason will I give for the postponement. Will Annie agree to a postponement?

We were picking up more girls as we crossed the school yard. I watched every girl standing along the route and prayed she didn't join the group. But of course, it seemed like everyone in the entire school wanted to watch me fight Annie.

Limbs surged up in the air like angry workers at an uprising. Some held tree branches. Others locked hands. Everyone talked and gestured with great animation. They wiped sweat off their faces with handkerchiefs or the back of their hands.

Annie was beaming. Why did I ever say a thing like that? Never before had I asked anyone to meet me at the back of the latrine. It wasn't the first time that a creole girl had made a comment about natives and dirt. I didn't even consider myself a native. Why did I react?

It seemed as if in all of Annie's eleven years of living, she had been waiting for my invitation to fight. I tried to feign her enthusiasm, but all I could think of was the cord around my waist. I had horrible images of Annie reaching for the gathers of my uniform as soon as we locked arms, pulling it up so that every girl could see my waist cord. Mary Bull leading the convulsive laughter. Annie's faction pointing to my cord.

"Look! Look. Look."

The shock and disappointment on the faces of my cheerleaders!

The crowd exploded into a *Hurray!* as we reached the steps of the latrine building. I don't remember if it was I who stopped, or if the uprising had just paused for the hurray, but as I faced the latrine corridor, a thought popped in my head.

"I want to use the latrine," I said, scurrying towards the steps.

"She wants to use the latrine! She wants to use the latrine!"

I darted up the steps. There was respite in my hurry. My body felt light. Maybe Annie noticed my sudden ease and panicked.

"I want to use the latrine, too," she said.

Then, of course, Mary Bull wanted to use the latrine, and Barbara wanted to use the latrine, and so did everyone else. The building had only about five cubicles. Soon, it looked like morning break, with girls lining up to use the latrine.

It must have been the out-of-school-hour line that attracted Mrs. Kissling.

"What are you girls still doing here?" She fanned her stick in front of us. "C'mon, go home. Each and every one of you."

We dispersed like rain-season flies. When we returned to school on Monday, new conflicts arose, and no one said much about the fight.

The First Interview

The clouds had broken open. It was their time. Muddy waters filled street gutters. The rainy season had arrived. Papa bought boxes of crackers, a gallon of gari, and a bottle of condensed Vimto. Our schools had closed, and we were going to be indoors most of the time. I cried all day.

"August baby," my parents teased me.

My twelfth birthday came, and of course, it rained even more tears. My cousins came from Boyle Street, Jenkins Street, and Cardew Street. We ate and drank to our hearts' content. We played records. We danced. I cried.

"Rainy season child."

My life was upside down. Schools will reopen in two weeks, and I did not yet have an interview. I might not be going to secondary school at all. Amie was already accepted into YWCA, and Mohammed would continue at Collegiate School. Their new uniforms and school supplies were ready to go.

"You should've applied for YWCA," Amie said.

"I don't want to learn how to cook and sew," I snapped.

Mohammed walked around the house, twisting his hips to dramatize the way my friends, Barbara, Joy, and Fredericka would be walking in their green and orange uniforms on the first day of school, while I stayed home.

I might end up like my mother.

Attatie gave a free bag of rice to someone whose wife worked at Annie Walsh School, so Mrs. Forster called me in for an interview. I skipped around the house. *Finally, I will be going to Annie Walsh School.*

On our way to the school, Papa reminded me to say, "Yes, please," instead of just, "Yes." Instead of saying "What?" say, "I beg your pardon, please, Mrs. Forster."

The room was spacious, with only two desks and a woman in front of a large typewriter.

"Mrs. Forster's on the telephone," she said to Papa.

We stood waiting. Five...fifteen...thirty...forty-five minutes...an hour. Meanwhile, the lady tapped away on the typewriter. Taxis blew their noisy horns outside. I moved over and stood by the window and passed the time looking past the bushy rows of tree on the schoolyard, to the closeup hands on the clock tower, to workers moving around inside the upper floor of Barclays Bank, and people going in and out of Small Police.

"You can go in now." The secretary managed a smile.

She was of small stature. Her hair was unmanageably short. Her spectacles sat on a pig-like nose. She looked up only after we had been standing there for about five or ten minutes. She picked up a paper here and put it back without looking at it, a file here, and returned it without opening it. She tremored with untamed emotion. She waved to a chair, only as an afterthought.

Papa sat. There were two chairs, but I couldn't sit face-to-face with a principal. I knew this one wouldn't want me to. I pierced my gaze into hers, the way I did when I wanted something from my parents. Like when I wanted to go to the Thanksgiving service.

Please, please, let me come to your school. I will behave myself, do whatever the teachers say. I will not act native. My friends, Fredericka, Joy, Barbara are all coming to this school.

"Wait outside, child."

"Yes, please, Mrs. Forster."

By the secretary's desk, I looked out of the window again. Clock Tower, the cars, Barclays Bank, Small Police. It will be only a short trip from Trinity School. I would stand in front of Trinity School and cross the road, at the Zebra, of course, past Daramola Studio, the Yoruba woman's street stall, the doctor's office, and there—Annie Walsh School. It would not be...

"Come on. Let's go," Papa said.

Maybe I refuse to remember the conversation with Papa on our way home. Maybe there was kola nut juice in Papa's mouth.

He held my hand firmly inside of his, and we walked the familiar route from Kissy Road. The cars honked. We got out of the way. Other passerbys went their ways. Some pushed. Some said excuse me. At Magazine Cut, someone from the Fadika house yelled a greeting. Papa yelled back. We walked on, ignoring the laboring clouds above. It was August, of course.

The Fight Comes to Attatie

Attatie now sewed only for those women who said things like, "No other seamstress can hide my stomach bulge the way you do," and those who shopped for their dresses and monthly rice purchases with her. She would remind us to do things like "Take off your school panties before going to Ilakow," and, "Lower your voice when you talk; you're a woman," between breaths as she licked a fingers to count her money.

Some of her comrades still implored her to "help change the country and not listen to those in-laws."

But Attatie replied, "I'm too busy with my rice trade and my sewing, and Mohammed's eyes are opening up too fast." This way, she stayed home and waited for the fight to come to her.

We were now awakened every morning by the blaring honk of lorries, taxis, and government Land Rovers, hoisting large green flags on their bumpers. Scruffy men piled on the vehicle hoods, wallpapered with the prime minister's campaign poster—an enormous head in the foreground of a water-colored serrated green trunk flanked by the letters SL and PP, under draping palm leaves. They were thrust about fifty or so to a lorry meant for twenty. Some of them swayed perilously on tailgates. They played the *kellie* and banged on the vehicles' metal panels, to party songs that espouse *One country, one people*, and the SLPP government's plan for a better Sierra Leone. They were young, mostly, some of secondary-school age. They held beer pints and smoked cigarettes.

A similar convoy would follow just after Goree Street had settled down, except for the poster, which entailed a man with a big nose, center-staged beside a flaming red half-sun with the words *All People's Con-*

133

gress on its base. Scores of taxis replaced the government Land Rovers in their convoy, but the lorries held a similar load of bucolic men. They sang an end to the high prices of food and the divisions of tribalism.

Attatie would stand up and make a fist to this group.

"APC must win," she said.

My siblings and I would jump up and wave the little red flags she had brought us from her rallies.

Sometimes she held conversations with the more mature men of the group.

"Thank you," she said to one, who said his name was Brima. "For the fight. For our country."

"Mama," Brima replied in a crass country accent. "This is our fight, too. We will not stop until APC wins."

He shot a finger to the clouds, then rambled on about one extraordinary feat after another he had committed in the name of the APC, like beating up SLPP supporters in the provinces, and helping open up roads that had been barricaded against APC campaigner workers. Attatie nodded and made sounds like *"Ehehhhhhh!"* and, *"Mmmhmm!"* and, "Waytin daat?"

There was a tailor shop next door to Mammy Porter's house. The master tailors together had eight or twelve young apprentices from the country. The young men ate at the shop and slept under the sewing machine tables. Attatie called them wild, too free, and uncivilized. When they argued, she would pull us inside the house and close the door. They spoke mostly in curse words. And when they laughed, it was with the kind of hilarious abandon that Attatie said came only from uncivilized country people.

"My name is Sayo," said one of those apprentices who was now a part of the APC convoy. He was standing against our fence, grinning. It was the first time I had seen any of those apprentices closeup. He was tall and lanky, about secondary-school age, with a flat nose.

"I'm APC." He waved his red flag.

"We are APC, too." I waved my red flag, then turned to see if Attatie had seen what was happening.

"You're creole?" he said.

"We're Mandinga!" I replied with triumph.

"I'm Limba." He was still grinning.

"Our houseboy is Limba, like Siaka Stevens." I grinned and noticed Attatie now looking in my direction.

"You're creole," Sayo said.

"Siaka Stevens is going to be our next prime minister," I said, avoiding a response.

I didn't know how to respond to such a statement from a person with whom I was sharing a common fight.

"You go to school," he said.

"I go to Trinity School," I said with pride.

"Then you're a creole."

"My father is a Mandinga, and my mother is a Soso," I said.

"You speak Mandinga?"

'No."

"Soso?"

"No."

Granny had always made clear I was Mandinga, even if she never followed it up with a language lesson. That, together with Islamic lessons, had been my tag so far. I had never before made the connection between being a Mandinga and speaking the language. Indeed, when it came to the existence of tribes, it was to me, then, an obscure phenomenon. Except for my Soso relatives, my interactions were only with Granny's tenants, whom I had picked up were Temne and Fullah peoples. There was Sorie black whom she often called, "one of the few Temne people you could reason with." And Kortor, an ascetic, unmarried middle-aged Fullah for whom Granny returned to the kitchen in old age because he refused to break his Ramadan fasting with food cooked by the equally unmarried Aminata.

In spite of the friendly relationship that was sprouting between us, I resented this bucolic boy with whom I considered myself worlds apart, pointing out my shortcoming. I resented his meddling into my immature tribal consciousness. I tried to stop the conversation. *Maybe Attatie will look at me and point. "Have I not told you not to talk with strangers?"*

Before I could finish my thought, Attatie did look at me, and Sayo's hand began slipping off our fence pole, his body retreating.

"*Bo,* Sayo," Attatie said.

Incredible! It was not just the wool in her voice, the absence of antipathy that jolted me. It was also her use of the familiar term *bo,* to address one of the *uncivilized* boys from the tailor shop. I could have been listening to her cajole one of her comrades.

"We must fight for Siaka Stevens." She overlooked the distortion in the boy's face.

***

"Mama, I've just voted," Sayo reported to Attatie early on election day.

Attatie congratulated "my son," and even Papa was encouraging.

"Sayo, you've done the right thing," he said, to which Sayo eagerly responded that it was his duty now to go from one polling station to another in the East End and bring the latest news to Goree Street.

With that, he ran down the empty street, as vans with loudspeakers blasted "go vote to end tribalism," or, "go vote for a better Sierra Leone."

Schools were closed, the mood soon became festive as people gathered in front of their gates, on verandahs and porches, with transistors outblasting one another. Some animatedly projected the day's winners.

Neighbors asked each other, *have you voted yet?* Children asked adults, *have you voted yet?* Children joked with one another *Have you voted yet?*

From one person's mouth to another's ear, the results began to trickle in; someone or the other had just returned from where the ballots were being counted. APC had won the Tonkolili district. They even had the numbers: Seventeen thousand votes for the rising sun. It became a mantra, "Tonkolili seventeen thousand."

It was only the second time such a name had registered in my consciousness. The first time was when Attatie returned from the convention in Port Loko and said Tonkolili was another district she and her comrades will be visiting.

I repeated the line, "Tonkolili seventeen thousand" as if I was familiar with its geography.

On a full-page map of West Africa, with Sierra Leone a small dot on its western edge, and Freetown the only bolded word on it, I squinted into the page, trying to find the name Tonkolili on the map. I was nowhere gone when I heard a loud cheer coming from the street. The mouth-to-ear transistor had produced a new set of results.

APC has won Kambia district.

APC has won East I -- grandpa Morlai's district, and *APC has won East II,* our district.

It was jubilation all around. The news continued.

APC has won Moyamba. Papa could not contain himself.

"Shet!" he said. "Moyamba is a Mende district.

"Even the Mendes are deserting the Prime Minister," Mr. Tommy added.

We heard cheers as far away as Elba Street and Fourah Bah Road. More young men from the tailor shop stood in front of our house. We conversed as though we had never ignored their existence.

It was late, but the sun had not yet set. The Tarawally children, from upper Goree Street, came out, the Ashcrofts stood alert on their verandahs, MaAbel came out on her porch, Mammy Palmer stared wide eyed from her window, and so did Mammy Penina. Even Miss Fenellla altered her poised demeanor. Mr. Pinkney came out in short trousers and took his usual position on the empty lot in front of our house.

Sayo had returned from his inspection of polling stations to join his friends to entertain us in a *Limba* dance -- raising a lively foot to the beat of the drums, one step at a time, back bent, arms and legs akimbo. From the verandah, Attatie danced with them. The entire street clapped, danced, and laughed, as one.

A vehicle covered in red cloth rolled slowly down the street. One of its occupant sang an APC campaign song through a loudspeaker. Shoulders swung and heads swayed, as Goree Street hummed and sang along, in Temne.

The next day, the newspaper man came. People threw coins at him more quickly than he could distribute papers. In a few minutes, he was out of *We Yone* newspapers. No one touched the Daily Mail.

Towards sunset, palm wine mingled with cigarette smoke in the air on Goree Street. Shouts of *AA! PP! CC! APC!* soared above the cadence of drums and the honk of vehicle horns. Red flags flooded the street. Children bounced up and down as if they'd been promised new shoes. The country's only radio station had just livestreamed the BBC news reel that gave the elections to APC, by two seats.

By daybreak the next day, people came out unto the streets to cry *foul!* and *The BBC never lie,* and *The BBC already said it. APC won! What is this that the Daily Mail is printing?* Mr. Tommy came hissing and swearing, his transistor held up to his ears. Grandpa Borbor arrived with his own transistor and declared himself ready for a fight to the death. Papa fumbled with the knobs of the living room radio. It was as if everyone was hoping for a different result from his individual radio.

While the collective transistors hissed long and crackled hard, we could hear, loud and clear, a boastful Sekou Turay on Radio Guinea coming from the Tarawally family up the road. Some people said it was a scary reminder of one-party muscle.

***

For another day or two, the government-controlled radio and newspaper continued to give the Palm Tree the lead. *We Yone* and the BBC gave the lead to the Rising Sun. For most of the morning, Papa's legs made six with that of the radio's legs in the living room.

We had fried eggs without bread for breakfast. The houseboy had stopped coming to work. Stores had shut down. Those who did, doubled their prices.

Papa got dressed for work and Attatie told him to be careful. Mr. Tommy stopped by too, on his way to work and received the same caution.

Papa had merely left when I heard quickened footsteps and loud noises of "kill all the Limbas and kill all the Mendes." Men in green and red shirts were huddled together in a scuffle. They attacked each with fists, stones, and vulgar words. Attatie joined the voices from the verandas calling on APC men for calm. The elderly men from both parties jumped in to disperse the crowd.

Then I saw Sayo wrestling with another man in green who had blood running down his cheeks.

"*Limbas* are big fools," shouted the Palm Tree man after they were separated.

"*Mende* frog eater," Sayo returned, blood streaks dripping from his gum.

As he was being hurled away, he threw a fist in the air and shouted, "This is Limba country."

The man in green shouted, "This is Mende country."

Later that day, as supporters called out the numerous towns the Rising Sun had captured, Port Loko, Bombali, Koinadugu, Kenema, Pujehun, Kambia, Kono, Bonthe, Kailahun, and Bo, I realized that I was hearing most of those names for the first time. My geography lessons at school had focused on Europe, and my Civics lessons stressed the importance of the city, its people, and its language. For me, nothing existed outside the boundaries of Freetown.

***

We heard that the country's twelve Paramount Chiefs were to vote on Tuesday. Whichever party got the most vote wins. *That will settle things,* it was said.

Except that, that did not settle things. The newspaper man came on Tuesday morning. Even the Daily Mail got snatched up this time. Mr. Tommy and Mr. Pinkney installed themselves in the middle of Goree Street. A bump, scruffy man in green and white tie-dye shirt hurled bitter Mende words at a lanky opponent who responded in Temne, with equal acidity.

"What are they saying?" I asked Attatie.

"I don't speak Mende," she said. Then, as if to translate for me, the one shouted "your mother's ass," and the other, "Your mother's vagina."

Attatie pushed us inside to "go open your books."

In the bedroom, my mind rejected the long division problem I tried to solve. The words on my *First Aid in English* seemed dormant. Even the stories on my Reader lay dead, compared to the live lesson going on outside.

"Who are the Paramount Chiefs?" I tried to justify my return to the living room.

"They rule the country people," Attatie said, and Papa tried to explain that they were mostly pre-colonial ruling families that the British colonial government acknowledged. Attatie didn't see the need for their individual votes to determine the final election results.

All the same, the Paramount Chiefs voted, all but two in favor of the ruling government.

Listen to your radio. 5 p.m. today!

Listen to your radio. 5 p.m. The loudspeaker was attached to a Land Rover.

Siaka Stevens will speak to you at 5 pm. Siaka Stevens will speak at 5 pm. Open your radios.

It was only about noon. The wait was already tense, before Mr. Tommy shove his head through the back door and whispered, "Have you heard? Siaka Stevens is going to be appointed Prime Minister."

Papa returned from work and described riot police on the streets.

It wasn't quite 5 o'clock when the radio began playing "I will exalt thee, Realm of the Free." Amie and I stood up, as we had been taught in school, but Mohammed and our parents remained seated. Mr. Tommy rushed in and sat down as if the chair cushions were made of eggs.

"Martial Law," the radio said. "Stevens is not Prime Minister."

The speaker called himself The Force Commander.

"Elections incomplete. Stop the rumors," he commanded. "Stop the demonstrations... Or bloodshed."

We heard the gunshots soon after.

"Our country's done spoiling," Papa said.

"Mortal Man!" Attatie sighed. "Nobody wants to give up power."

"The krios will not put up with this," Mr. Tommy said.

The national anthem came on a second time, and Force Commander, Brigadier Lansana, he said his name was, repeated his fiat.

"Martial law. Stevens is not Prime Minister. Elections incomplete. Stop street demonstrations. Stop spreading rumors. Or bloodshed." He swore to God.

***

There was a heavy knock on our back door early the next morning. Rumors had been circulating of soldiers taking opposition supporters from their homes to be shot. Attatie was no longer involved with politics, not outside of the house, at least, but I was still concerned for her. Mohammed rushed to the door. I was right behind him. A woman stood at the door. Her top and bottom clothing did not match. The top was of a dark brown lilac, with a shoulder strap hanging down her right arm, and her wrapper and headtie had a green background with large black leaves. She looked like a market woman, a native woman. Next to her was a scruffy man, with the thin features of a Fullah. His rags made him out to be a laborer who carried people's wares on his head.

But these were changing times.

Attatie was speaking in familiar terms with Sayo, the krios on Goree Street, even from their high veranda and windows, were joining in the tune of a Temne song. Miss Fenella was talking to the boys from the tailor shop. Sayo, a Limba, was standing up to a Mende man. This market woman and this laborer might not be as they appeared.

"I need a bag of rice," the woman said, "I hear there's going to be bloodshed."

Atttie rushed to the door. "I hope you're supporting the APC," she said, observing the woman's clothes. "You know that Siaka Stevens is going to help all the market women in the country."

The woman traced a family tree that connected her to Stevens' running mate, S.I. Koroma.

Pleased with the woman's anestory, Attatie now expressed concern.

"Are you not afraid to leave your house at a time like this?"

"I have no food for the children," the woman said, and the conversation quickly moved to talk of support for the Rising Sun in her neighborhood.

Throughout the day, customers dribbled in and out through the back door to pick up a bag of rice and with that, the latest news on the elections. A man who came in the afternoon told us, "I hear the Prime Minister has sworn not to give up power to the Opposition."

The Force Commander

The sound seemed to come from under my pillow. It was like a thunder gone mad. I stepped on Amie's legs to make my way to the verandah. In the living room, Papa was dressed for work, with a mashed-up face glued to the radio set.

"Don't open that door," he hollered.

It was too late. An army of men already had their gun muzzles pointed over my head. Before Papa could yank me away from the door, I saw those wild muddy faces that had attacked my mother. I saw her turning her head to escape the punch, only to meet the butt of another soldier's gun waiting on the other side. I understood the bloodied bruises she had brought home. It was the first time I experienced hate; hate for those muddy faces like groundnuts, just dug up from dirt and bolstered with rifles.

"Get out of there!" Papa shot the door.

I tried to regain my composure on the chair I had landed.

"Go do your homework," he said.

"The common entrance exams are over," I said. "I don't need to study anymore."

"As long as you're in school......"

It was hard to compare school to what I was learning on Goree Street.

We had just finished another breakfast when my siblings and I stood up for the National Anthem. It was the Force Commander again. He called on "all new parliamentarians" to "Ring 6381."

He repeated the number "6381. "Ask for Brigadier David Lansana," he said, and they'll be given an address for a meeting.

"Don't go anywhere," Papa screamed at the radio. "It's a bloody trap. He's going to have all APC parliamentarians shot."

The National Anthem ended the Force Commander's message, but it was only a few minutes before he returned.

"Curfew order!"

He commanded everyone to stay home from dusk to dawn, or the force will spill blood on the streets.

The Police Commissioner followed. "We have no alternative but to fall in line," he said. "That is all."

Papa hissed.

Attatie decried mortal man.

Goree Street became cold and dark. Everyone stayed in-doors. Gunshots crackled in the near distance.

People came out in the morning and cried foul play. Like school children united under punishment, they responded with mockery.

Did you hear that? He cannot pronounce curfew. He said coffee order. The crass countryman! Do we have coffee order today? No today is Ovaltine order. Tomorrow, Cocoa order.

At dusk, everyone retired to the security of their homes, and gun-wielding soldiers took over the dark streets. At daybreak, rumors circulated of people shot on the threshold of their gates, others while returning home from a late-night shift.

"Siaka Stevens is going to be shot," Mr. Tommy waved his arms vigorously in the air.

Attatie dropped the teacup she was wiping. Papa's eyes bloodied. Word was that the government planned to take Siaka Stevens to a remote location somewhere in the middle of the night and shoot him.

Angry men filled Goree Street again. They carried knives and sticks, cement blocks and stones.

We're going to block the roads! We're going to block the roads! They're not taking Siaka Stevens anywhere.

The next day. The national anthem.

Force Commander Brigadier Lansana under arrest, the radio said.

Prime Minister Margai under arrest.

Governor General under house arrest.

Siaka Stevens to be installed Prime Minister.

A fresh jubilation would have broken out on Goree Street, except for what came right after.

The National Anthem.

Army still in charge, police still with them.

Curfew order still in place. All political activities banned.

He was a brand-new commander. He declared the elections results a tie, and said they exhibited too much tribalism. Everyone to remain calm, he said, and turn a new page.

The transistor volumes soared. People pored over old newspapers for hidden answers. Everyone rubbed their chins.

Whatever is happening in the country? Who's really in charge?

Maybe they will release Siaka Stevens now.

Maybe Albert Margai will come back.

No, wait, maybe it's a trick. They arrest Lansana and bring Margai back.

Oh, no, maybe, the British are coming back. Maybe they are behind all this mess.

The National Anthem.

Another brand-new commander.

He said his name was Major Blake. Charles Blake. *A British name. A krio?*

No, he's Mende. The Mende will never give up power.

Maybe he's just a stand in for Albert Margai.

Maybe he's standing in for the British.

Maybe the British should take over again. Best for everyone.

Another day or so.

The national anthem again.

Colonel Juxon-Smith said something he called the National Reformation Council had taken over the country.

Martial law – stop the bloodshed – stop corruption – stop tribalism – continue curfew order.

Juxon who? National what?

Slowly, the young men began returning to the tailor shop. Sayo didn't come back. A bullet to his chest as he stood in front of an army truck he believed was carrying Stevens to be shot.

***

Colonel Juxon-Smith vowed to "rectify the moral aspect of the State." I didn't know what that meant, and neither did most of the adults around me. Soon, the Colonel deployed a heavy artillery of guns, religion, and speeches. The country succumbed to the sight of guns everywhere, and bucolic army men in sparkling Mercedes Benz.

The Colonel transformed Victoria Park into a construction site for a church and mosque neighboring each other—for harmony.

And then there were the speeches; speech after speech touting death to tribalism, the termination of corruption, the elimination of nepotism, and the need for sweat and blood work. He said he had come to buck us up.

The country the colonel had taken by force came out of independence to be led by a genteel, affable, Mende doctor called Milton Augustus Strieby Margai. Affable Milton passed away a decade into his rule, to be succeeded by a less amiable younger half-brother. Under three years into Albert Margai's rule people were blaming the Mendes for the country's growing pains. This was in the mid-sixties, when laborious British names like Cassandra Victoria Johnson-Coker and Septimus Sylvanus McEwen ran the civil service. Such names meant a missionary school had molded you into a person that could read the Bible and write those letters needed to buttress the waning colonial enterprise. The truth is that there were more freed Africans from Jamaica, Nova Scotia, and Britain with British names than were Mendes.

There was also that mélange of Africans, Muslims and Christians, rescued from slave ships off the Atlantic in the early 1800s. They joined the mostly Muslim inhabitants of what was later to be called Freetown – the Temne, Mandinga, Soso, Fullah, Yalunka, Kuranko, and together, they established western schools like those that Christian missionaries had created for freed slaves.

Soon their children relegated their Islamic education to evening and Sunday morning lessons as they aspired to those civil service positions held by the Mendes and the freed slaves.

If you were one of those many young men and women raised up-country without access to the few missionary schools they had in your town, coming to the city meant you lived like the Tailor Shop boys, you worked as a house servant, or you found some other menial job on which to survive. The women came into the city mostly as wives and mothers.

Might this be the "moral aspect" the Colonel wanted to "rectify?" For the APC supporters on Goree Street, the thirty-six-year-old Colonel had neither the experience nor the skill for the job.

The Colonel's Church and Mosque construction went ahead amidst rumors that Stevens had been expelled to neighboring Guinea.

***

It wasn't long before we were stopping on our way from school, to play around the two abandoned structures on the grounds of Victoria Park. Boys would throw small crumbling pieces at each other, and we would have to cover our eyes against the flying sand dunes. Some of us made benches out of the low parapet, and others jumped hurdles over them.

The announcement had come, like all others, after the national anthem. The red shirts and red flags re-emerged on Goree Street. Country people and Freetown people, wrappers and skirts, headties and hats danced under the torrid sun. There were guitars and tin drums on the streets again, as were the *shegures* and xylophones. Every transistor was back at blast level.

I remember certain parts of the speech that came over the radio.

"I believe that it is a providential coincidence that the seventh anniversary of the independence of this our dear country should coincide with the return to constitutional rule," Prime Minister Stevens began.

Papa grinned.

"We are grateful to the almighty Allah for the guidance He has given us...."

For the first time, I heard the word "Allah" on the radio.

The Second Interview

The taxi ride to Wilberforce was through a downtown submerged under the heavy afternoon sun. Working women in uniforms. Men buttoned up in white shirts and ties, straddled between potholes and broken sidewalks. They ignored the persistent car horns of hurried taxi drivers. They talked animatedly and waved off exhaust smoke with their hands.

Papa tried to make conversation—as if I didn't know that Barclays Banks staff wore blue, and Commercial Bank staff, gold.

"I've never before gone past Clock Tower to reach my school," I said, returning to the matter at hand.

He called my attention, instead, to the courthouse and the Cotton Tree.

"Isn't it big?" he said.

I agreed. The Cotton Tree is Freetown's baobab. Five busy roads meet at its roots—*the perfect place to scatter Attatie's fangadama.*

"And look at the Statehouse!" he said.

It's like a white camel atop a gentle slope.

"Impressive," I replied, sulking.

He showed me the flag on the American Embassy, and the Sierra Leone Museum, which looked like a toybox.

"You will see these interesting sights every day on your way to school."

I refused to get out of the car.

"This is your only choice." Papa pulled me by the elbow. "This is my second choice."

I got out and waited for him to pay the driver.

Thick tree bushes covered a pastel-green building. It reminded me of stories about children getting lost in bushes. As we walked up the sprawling flight of brick steps, I decided it was a scary place for a secondary school.

Inside the building, a twiggy secretary with an elongated neck sat behind a gloomy stretch of glass windows that did little to brighten the room. Still, the twiggy lady wore dark glasses. She wasn't expecting us, and she jerked off her chair, adjusted her dark glasses, and greeted us with the voice of a crying pepper bird, all in one swoop. Papa gave his name, and she hopped through a tight space between her desk and a door marked *Principal*.

The word *Principal* made my skin crawl. *Mrs. Forster*, I thought.

"Mrs. Collier will see you now, sir," the secretary chirped.

My face was still rumpled when I entered Mrs. Collier's office.

The positioning of her desk forced you to meet eye-to-eye with the streak of silky gray that side-parted her full head of black hair. Then her eyes, like two bubbly malt balls, surged to meet you. And her plum lips, red with lipstick, parted to reveal a muscular set of teeth.

"Are you enjoying your holidays?" She wouldn't let my gaze wander around the room.

My thoughts, instead, tried to roam—back to Trinity School, to Miss Jackson, to Mrs. Forster. But the malt balls held steady, like I was the only being in its orbit.

"Yes, I'm enjoying my holidays." I smiled.

She followed up with questions. First, about my favorite hobbies, which I told her were reading and writing. Then on to my favorite subjects. I felt like the cleverest girl in the class, as that silver streak moved approvingly with one answer after the other. By the time she asked if I would like to come to her school, I had already contrived answers as to why I wanted to come to Methodist Girls High School—like the long, beautiful driveway, the expanse of fruit trees, the helpful, whirling secretary, and yes, the principal herself.

Outside Mrs. Collier's office, the secretary hopped back and forth gingerly as Papa bought the checkered mauve-and-white uniform fabric, the black belt and beret, and a mauve ribbon and crest for my straw hat.

Yellow cashew flesh littered the street, and ripe mangoes hung low on the trees of the ten-minute walk down the school driveway into Main Motor Road. As we waited for a taxicab, it dawned on me that other than the good-afternoon greetings, Mrs. Collier had ignored Papa throughout the interview. The entire thirty-minute conversation had been between my principal and me.

What the Schools Are Doing These Days

A few days before school started, my cousin, Rugie, accompanied me on my second visit to Methodist Girls High School. Parents and pupils strolled around the campus carrying large raffia and paper bags. We joined a line that stretched from the first-floor entrance of the administrative building to a classroom on the second floor wrapped in the chemical smell of new books. While we waited, Rugie studied my booklist, and I studied the crowd for new friends. It was mostly a West End crowd, but it didn't bother me. Not after my one-on-one conversation with Mrs. Collier.

Mrs. Collier's secretary was in the room, in a stir. Through her dark glasses, she peered into the eyes of the buyer in front of her, before taking the booklist. Then, for some unknown reason, she would make a jerky roundabout turn, with the booklist in hand, before wiggling back to the buyer. She dropped books on the ground and counted money incessantly. She would close the money tin, only to immediately remember that the customer needed change.

Few of the parents seemed to pay attention to the clumsy secretary. The mood was lively, and most of the parents seemed more into the conversations they were having.

I was standing next to a woman whose voice soared above all the others. She had on a wig, it seemed. Her daughter, boney, with straight braids that ran from her forehead to her neck, held on tight to her arm. The woman was talking to a man who kept pulling up his trousers.

"All of this was nothing but bushes when I was in school here." She spoke so loudly, most people turned around to look toward the window.

Another woman added a description of the churchyard school where she said it all started, somewhere in the middle of town. Other parents joined in, and soon, they were outflanking each other on details of the history of the school.

By the time we moved a few steps up the line, I heard another conversation behind me.

"I'm an old boy of Grammar School," a man said, "but I spent a lot of money, and had to talk to a number of contacts before my son could enter that school."

The woman responded with a story about a niece who was refused an interview at Methodist Girls High School, even though she and her sister went to the school.

"It's not right what the schools are doing these days," she said. "Bringing in children whose parents didn't attend *our* schools."

The man sighed. "Too many native children in schools these days."

I wished the line would move forward so I could buy my books and run away.

"My daughter is a Methodist," the man continued, "and she has to go to Freetown Secondary School for Girls."

"It's not right," the woman repeated.

Leah Street

During my last year at Holy Trinity School, we moved to a new house at Leah Street.

"Hold on, hold on." Attatie put a hand in front of Amie and I.

We were holding our portmanteaus, ready to bustle into the front door. Attatie held a bowl of water, with one hand dipped inside.

"We're here." She called on Siminie Sillah, Karimu Sillah, Mameh Sillah, and all the other ancestors. "We're going to occupy this new house." She sprinkled water on the walls, on the ceramic floor tiles, on the white casement windows, and the ceiling. "Protect us and our children."

Amie and I followed her impatiently through the house until she reached our bedroom.

"This is the room my daughters will occupy." She sprinkled water on the walls, and even on our beds. "Protect them in here. Do not allow any bad spirits to enter this room."

I was used to watching Papa working hard in the living room, plotting lands and designing houses for others. When it came to our own house, everyone had a say.

"I want my own bedroom right here." I stamped a finger on the tracing paper.

Amie snatched Papa's pencil and drew another box at the farthest end of the paper.

"This is my bedroom right here."

Papa got back his pencil and wrote inside of another box in the center of the paper.

Amie and Mameh's bedroom.

"I don't want to share a room with her," I said. "She'll continue to wear my clean panties.

"She'll keep the lights on, reading, when I want to sleep," Amie said.

Mohammed selected a downstairs bedroom, away from everyone.

"You're going upstairs, where we can keep an eye on you," Attatie said.

And Papa removed his finger from the bottom of the paper to an upstairs box.

"Then who's going to be in that room downstairs?" Mohammed grimaced, pointing to a box without a name.

Papa hesitated, then said, "Visitors."

"That is Granny Kadi's room," Attatie said.

***

Attatie's hairdresser took care of the Christian guests at the opening-house ceremony. She was tall and stocky, with very short hair. They had known each other since girlhood and continued to be friends and clients of each other.

Attatie's hairdresser friend was one of those embroidered print-dress clients who also became a rice customer. The hairdresser's husband and Papa attended Prince of Wales school together. Reasons, Attatie explained, why they were our aunty and uncle.

Aunty Marion also sold Star beer, Heineken, and Guinness Stout to make ends meet, at the salon, which was in a corner of her living room, on Patton Street.

At dawn on Sunday, when the aunties and friends were arriving to help with the cooking, Attatie left for Aunty Marion's salon. She supervised the dishing up on her return, then changed changed into a turquoise lace gown with sparkling sequins—a dress, she said, together with the new house, buttoned her new status as a hardworking woman.

Papa wore his usual tie-dye rappel, which made him look like a mere guest, especially compared to his uncles, who wore the longer flowing kaftan.

The *sara* prayers for the new house were held in the downstairs living room. Afterwards, while Aunty Fatmata and Aunty Mariama distributed the food and drinks among the women, Papa's uncles took charge of the male guests. They distributed the jollof rice which the men ate two to a bowl. Then they placed the drinks, kola nuts and *fourah*, together with donations collected during the qur'an reading in small wicker baskets: a basket for the Mandinga men, one for the Mende men, a basket for the Sosos, another for the Temnes, a basket for the Fourah Bay people, another for the Limbas, a basket for the Fullah Town people, one for the Fullahs, and another for the Lokkos. Each tribe received the same amount of food and money, regardless of the number of men present. There was only one man from the Lokko tribe, and he carried the entire basket of food. But everyone said the tradition must be followed and joked that his ancestors were with him that morning.

The upstairs space and veranda were reserved for those guests who did not participate in the qur'anic prayers—creoles and Christians, mostly—who arrived in the afternoon and evening to be served alcohol.

Attatie changed into a gold brocade top and wrapper and showed off her entire head of glistening curled hair. As she moved up and down the ceramic staircase, making sure the women downstairs had food parcels to take home, and welcoming arriving upstairs ones, a bearded man with a heavy copper face arrived with his wife at his side.

"Do you know this man?" she said to me.

I did not recognize him.

"This is Mister Johnson-Cole," she said. And this is his wife, Margaret."

I gave the usual well-brought-up nod—a congenial smile with a slight head-tilt.

"Good afternoon, sir," I replied. "Good afternoon, ma."

"He works at the Examinations Council," Attatie continued.

"Oh," I said.

Papa had seen a friend at the Examinations Council to help me get into Methodist Girls High School.

I smiled broadly and responded with enthusiasm when he asked if I was doing well at Methodist Girls High School.

Attatie directed Aunty Marion to pay particular attention to Mr. and Mrs. Johnson-Cole.

As the upstairs guests increased, Attatie asked me to help Aunty Marion with the serving. I would stand by her side in the room where the food and drinks were stored and help her put six or seven medium-sized paper plates into a large tray. Into each plate, she put a serving of jollof rice, with one piece of fish, chicken, and beef. On the side of the rice, she added a slice of rice bread, a slice of pound cake, meat and fish balls, and pieces of shrimp chips. I carried the tray to the living room and served a plate to each guest. Of course, I smiled broadly again when serving the Johnson-Coles.

The upstairs conversations got lighter and louder as it darkened outside, until Aunty Marion's husband left without her, and Attatie's bosom Muslim and Christian girlfriends began trickling into the downstairs space. The new settees and side stools had been put back after the prayer mats were removed. Aunty Fatmata and a woman in a short dress and cornrowed hair occupied a sofa, Aunty Mariama and Aunty Ijatu another, and the rest took individual setteees and chairs. I made several trips up and down the stairs, bringing pints of alcohol and glasses to fill the center table.

"Why did he leave so soon?" Aunty Fatmata said, being sarcastic.

"Why else?" replied the woman in the short dress. "To go see her, of course."

She had a cigarette in one hand, and a pint of Star beer in another.

"There's nothing you can do," Aunty Mariama said."

As they poured beer into glasses and smoked cigarettes, every woman gave testament to her depth of despair of the male breed. Everyone agreed with everyone else's general distrust of the patriarchy, and they concluded that whether a man is Muslim or Christian, they're all children of the same mother.

Attatie and Aunty Marion joined them, leaving Papa and the few remaining men upstairs. Aunty Marion had a pint of Heineken in the hand holding her handbag, and a cigarette in the other.

As she sat down, Aunty Ijatu said, "You're not leaving us so soon, are you?"

"What duckass am I chasing?" She sucked into her cigarette.

"At least you don't have to worry about him marrying the sweetheart," Aunty Mariama said.

At which point, Attatie said not all Muslim women worry about their husbands eventually marrying his sweetheart. As for her, she said, after all the work she has put into lifting up the family to a house like this, her husband will have to give that endeavor an extraordinary amount of thought if he counted on a long and peaceful life.

They broke into boisterous laughter which must have reached Papa and the men upstairs.

The conversation soon went back to Aunty Marion, and a focus on pulling her together, telling her she was not alone in her dilemma, that her husband will soon become tired of the other woman and return to her. In the meantime, she was advised to focus on her children and her business. Aunty Marion nodded, took a long draw on her cigarette, and opened another pint of Heineken.

Granny Kadi's Promise

On our last Sunday on Goree Street, Attatie stood on the foot of the kitchen steps and conducted a meeting with Granny Kadi.

"As you know, Granny Kadi, we'll be moving to the new house at Leah Street."

Granny Kadi paused, a knife in one hand, potato leaves in another.

"Yes, I know. And we thank Allah for opening the way so quickly for a young couple like you. We pray that he continues to bless the new home and young family in it."

"Ameena, Ameena," Attatie said. "What I want to tell you is this." Her voice was now stern. "We do not want alcohol or snuff in the new house."

Granny Kadi put down the knife and potato leaves. Gently, she clasped her hands and put them down between her legs.

"By the grace of Allah," she said, "I have thought about it myself. I'm not a young woman anymore. I've decided that, with Allah's help, I will stop drinking and I will cut down on the snuff."

"Inshallah," Attatie said. "Because how do you think the new house will look in the eyes of good people if *omole* drinkers are always coming in and out of our yard?"

"Inshallah," said Granny Kadi, "Allah will not allow that to happen."

I had already visited the new house. Its cemented compound contrasted it with the dirt ground on Goree Street. The image of Granny Kadi's snuff spit splattered on the cement, not to mention her bedroom being opposite the dining room, had caused my blood to boil enough for me to raise concern with Papa and Attatie.

***

We settled down in the new house. Papa, now a senior licensed surveyor, made no more up-country tours. His private clientele ballooned with more space for his plane table, tools, and maps. And Attatie was setting up a store as full-time rice trader.

That left my siblings and I at the mercy of Granny Kadi. Except for her closest friend, a former Soso dancer who sometimes entertained Attatie with songs and dance, Granny Kadi appeared to have cut off the Goree Street clientele. If she still drank *omole* or ate snuff, it was in discreet space, at a generous distance.

Mrs. Coker

"Good morning, Mrs. Coker."

"Remove your fingers from the desks and straighten your backs."

Everyone penciled up.

Her stumpy index finger fanned the classroom, her determined gaze cutting through our eager faces like a new blade. "I hope you've all come here to do well," she said.

Right away, this short-haired grandmother in round spectacles, erect over the teacher's desk, dampened my enthusiasm for the new school. Methodist Girls High School was known for its stern teachers and studious students, but I wasn't expecting to be gathered up on the first morning of school. I knew none of the girls in the classroom, and I feared already that it might be all schoolwork here and no time for friendships.

"You may sit," Mrs. Coker said.

It was a trap.

She pursed her lips, her mouth resolute as she waited on our slow, deliberate descent. She absorbed the noise we made dragging our iron chairs on the cement floor.

Then finally, with squinted eyes, she said, "Get up again. Each and every one of you, get up!"

It is the first thing every girl learns about the MGHS uniform. Unless you're one of those aloof, *clever* girls who had taken the Common Entrance Exam at nine or ten years old, or you were one of those unkept girls, you paid great attention to your pleats. They must always look starched and straight, and much care must always be taken, especially before sitting down, that they are in place so they do not rumple.

"Now sit down again," Mrs. Coker said, "without touching those pleats."

A confused quiet enveloped the room. I turned to the girl on my right, then on my left. Everyone turned to everyone else for direction. Didn't the starched pleats go with the prestige of being an MGHS girl? Do we dare walk the streets with rumpled pleats?

"Sit down," I said.

My bottom landed on the wooden chair seat like lead dropped on sand from a flying plane. Luckily, the starched pleats formed a cushion between my backside and the chair. Every other girl sat down, hugger-mugger, and quickly returned to Mrs. Coker's orbit.

"My name is Florence Coker. I started teaching at this school before any of you were born." She shoved up her spectacles. "I taught some of your mothers."

Couldn't have been mine.

"I'm very proud of the pupils who have passed through me," she said, "and of what they became. I remain in contact with them, even after they get married and have children of their own." She paused. "I never forget a pupil."

I doubted any of my Trinity School teachers remembered me, even when I was in the classroom. This woman was vowing to remember me, even after I leave this school. My skin crawled.

"I want to know your names," she said.

Names? Was she trying to weed me out?

"My name is Margaret." The corn-rowed girl in front of me said, her chin pointing to the ceiling.

"Millicent is my name," the girl behind her said.

Elizabeth, then Flora, then Cecilia, and Dorothy.

Thank God I had not taken a seat close to the teacher. I was seated not at the back, not close to the window, not close to the door. I was right in the middle, where I could blend and Mrs. Coker would ignore me, like I was used to.

The introduction reached me. "My name is Memuna."

"My name is Glynis," the girl next to me said.

"My name is Fannianette."

"My name is Theodora."

"My name is Williette."

"My name is Memuna Kamara."

"My name is Florence."

If there were children of her former students in the room, Mrs. Coker showed no particular interest in them.

"It's not enough to wear a secondary school uniform," she said, after the introductions. "It is not enough to stiffen your uniform pleats with starch and shake your hips like glamor girls." She cupped her resolute mouth again and pushed back her spectacles. "You must, above all, perform." She hit her knuckles against the table. "Perform with high standards if you are to remain in this school."

I was entranced. *My mind is made up. I will begin to heed Attatie's words and make no friendship other than with my books. Nothing, whatsoever, will come between me and my ability to perform. I will prove myself to Missus Coker. She will like me, in spite of my name.*

"From this day forward," she panned that fat index finger around the room again, "you are, and will comport yourselves, each and every one of you, like a Wesleyan girl."

A what girl? I'd never heard the word Wesleyan before. Yet I believed I was it. I was whatever girl Mrs. Coker wanted me to be.

"In this uniform," Mrs. Coker said, "your actions are reflected on every girl that ever walked the corridors of this school."

There were none of those girls I could imagine, especially not from my family. But somehow I felt I would connect to those old girls. *Mrs. Coker will see to it.*

"In this uniform, you do not eat in the streets, you do not speak a language other than English, and you talk only in soft voices."

Who *we* are, what *we* do, and what *we* wear. By the end of my first day at Methodist Girls High School, I had swallowed Mrs. Coker's kola nut juice, chaff and all.

***

The buses came and went. I did not fight my way in. I could not.

The English teacher, the biology teacher, the math teacher, the geography teacher, the physical education teacher each had her own books, her own rules, her own commands. Then there was Mrs. Grant, who made us look like confused fools for not understanding French on day one. The weight of a rigorous school was pulling me down on day one. I wished I was still in the one-teacher classroom of Trinity School.

The girls were but a wave of mauve and white uniforms in which I meandered, like a zombie, on the way down the school's driveway into Main Motor Road.

"Let's walk to Brookfields. It'll be easier to catch an empty bus there."

No, I'm afraid to walk on that bridge. Girls have fainted walking on it."

"We'll hold hands."

"But there are other schools there: FSSG, YWCA, Saint Joseph's Convent. They fill up the buses quickly."

"Let's walk to Congo Cross instead."

"That's worse! We'll have to fight with Collegiate and Grammar School boys.

"Let's just stand here and wait. There'll be an empty bus soon."

In the end, the ball of black berets splintered into several groups—some going toward the dizzying bridge; others opting to stay put; and others, to Congo Cross. I figured if there are Collegiate boys at Congo Cross, I might see Mohammed, and he'll help me get on a bus.

Congo Cross turned out to be a rusty tin roof spilling over with khaki shorts and white shirts, mauve tunics on white blouses, gray shorts and white shirts, and some of our mauve-and-white checkered that had preceded us. A double-decker arriving just as we reached the stop was already being jumped on by Collegiate and Grammar School boys, even before it came to a stop. Mohammed was not amongst them.

Under the roast of the torrid afternoon, some girls devised lofty alternative plans for getting home: taking a taxi, stopping a private car for a lift, hopping on a *podapoda*. My mind rushed to Mrs. Coker's lecture on *this uniform,* and I settled for the school bus. I moved the pain of my saddlebag from one shoulder to the other, squinted and endured the coming and departing of two or three other buses before, with the thinning crowd, I finally found the courage to fight my way into one.

It took me a few days to get into the routine of walking to Congo Cross after school and fighting to get on a bus. It was more than a week before I began to pay attention to the other girls who alighted at the

Clock Tower stop. That was when I met Glynis and Melissa. The two already knew each other from the neighborhood and church. Glynis had four brothers and two sisters, all with the same copper color, oval mouth, and tiny, dull eyes. The Godwins lived with their mother, an elementary school teacher, and a grandmother, in the single-story brick house right next to ours.

Melissa lived on Morgan Lane, a few minutes' walk from us. She had two elder siblings from her father's previous marriage, and one from her mother's previous marriage. Then there was her and three younger siblings from the current union. All seven children lived in the same house with the parents.

It wasn't long before Melissa, Glynis, and I were regulars in each other's homes. My parents reminded me to not eat pork when I visited them. Granny Kadi said I should not eat at all in what she called the *nansara* homes.

No Better Cook

Her first client at Leah Street, Sissy Baby, lived in one of the tin shacks in Glynis's yard. A Mende woman with breasts that draped her chest like a sisal bag of wet sand, she often covered her knee-length dresses with old wrappers that stopped above her ankle.

Granny Kadi would leave whatever she was cooking on the fire to answer her call over the cement wall, after which she would return from her bedroom, caressing a bulge the size of a tot pint under her wrapper.

One Saturday morning, when Papa and Attatie were away, Sissy Baby came to our house. Granny Kadi quickly shuffled out the flaming wood from the fire and left the slow-burning coal under the pot of bitters soup. During their tryst in her bedroom, I hovered around the dining table until they emerged balancing against each other and the hallway walls, leaving behind them the unmistakable waft of *omole*.

As soon as Attatie returned home, I described what I had seen.

"You're making a mistake," she said. "Granny Kadi has stopped drinking."

"No, she hasn't," I said. "And other *omole* drinkers are coming to our house again."

"Don't worry. I will talk with her. I will put it to her that we cannot have *omole* drinkers or sellers in this house."

I was sitting on the landing of the backdoor steps, watching Granny Kadi pound fresh pepper. She was sitting on a low bench, mortar inserted between her legs, one hand on its wooden rim, the other gripping the pestle. She was wearing one of her cooking wardrobe— an old mismatched top and wrapper with hem sitting high above her ankle to facilitate her movement. The moment she saw me, her muscle beef began moving violently over the mortar.

"This pepper that I'm pounding here so," she croaked, head bent over the hot pepper, as if to show invincibility. "This is a *sassa*." She pointed to the pepper inside the mortar. "This is the curse that will destroy those children who cannot keep their mouths shut."

The pestle hit the mortar with a bang that sent brown fluid and pepper seeds flying out. She did not blink.

I knew that only pepper, onions, and tomatoes are usually pounded in that mortar, but hard as I tried, I wasn't able to ignore the possibility that she had added this *sassa* thing into the mortar, and that I might be headed for the same predicament that plagued us after Mr. Conteh left Goree Street.

As if she read my thoughts, Granny Kadi made an elaborate move of untying the edge of her wrapper and emptying something I could not see into the mortar.

"Those children whose mouths have forgotten the bitter taste of kola nut juice." She was pounding now, tucking in her wrapper and adjusting her head tie.

At one point, she suspended the pounding altogether to undo the head tie, shake it out, and retie it in one violent move.

"I will put their mouths into this mortar with this *sassa* and grind it. Then I will shove the hot pepper up their ass." Her voice had peaked.

But I was in secondary school. I could separate those things I could see and repeat without consequence from those that should be keep quiet. Strangers coming to our house to purchase and drink alcohol was not something to keep quiet. Papa would disapprove of that, and so will Attatie and even Granny, if the word reached her. I was old enough to know that.

It was only a few Saturdays after Attatie promised to *put it* to Granny Kadi, that Sissy Baby returned. This time, she was accompanied by an emaciated woman with one of those parched lips and bruised faces that announced a seasoned *omole* drinker. Again, Granny Kadi drew firewood from under the sorrel soup pot, and the three women disappeared into her bedroom. This time, I brought Amie downstairs and we pressed our noses between the jamb and door panel to confirm the smell of alcohol, then waited for the women to come out dragging their feet on the tile.

Back in the kitchen, Granny Kadi tried to regain her seat on the low bench, and almost landed on the bare cement. Then she tried to pick up a calabash with raw rice in it. The calabash slipped from her hand and smashed into pieces. Now she attempted to gather the rice grains from the gutter edge, and her entire body landed on her right arm.

One thing that always amused Amie about Granny Kadi was the litany of new four-letter words we learned when she was drunk. Amie gleefully repeated those new curse words to Attatie later that day, when she, together with the broken calabash, bore witness to my story.

"I cannot afford to lose money," Attatie said. "Besides, there's no better cook in this town than Granny Kadi."

No better cook? Was the taste of her soup that important? Was she angry at me for telling on Granny Kadi?

Even Amie could not hold back.

"Soon, our house will be frequented by all the *omole* drunkards in the East End," she moaned.

Attatie gave neither of us the eye to continue the conversation.

"I cannot close the shop to stay home and cook," she said.

So Granny Kadi's friends and clients continued coming to the house when my parents were away, which was all day, every day, except Sunday, and Attatie's friends complimented her for keeping a professional grade cook.

Granny Kadi continued to bring us jollof rice, *foofoo*, bitters soup, *orbiata*, soft drinks, and other food from her cooking engagements. My siblings and I ate and giggled while she tripped around the yard and exposed us to new curse words.

When School Came Home

Upper Patton Street begins with a not-so-gentle slope at Kissy Road and turns into the massive hills of Mount Aureol. It is a landscape of boulders sunken into red dirt that becomes mud paste in the rainy season. Glynis's house sat right at the point where Leah Street cuts across Upper Patton Street's knee cap.

An elderly woman in a black round-neck dress stood in the middle of the road, arms akimbo. She appeared to be taking a breather, observing the daunting hill ahead, wondering, maybe, if she should have paid the extra fare for the taxi to take her further up. She removed her silver-rimmed glasses and wiped sweat off her face with a clean white handkerchief. Then she dipped her head inside her neck, pulled up a handbag over the right shoulder, and soldiered on.

Wait! Heeeeey! It's Missus Coker. She's turning into Leah Street.

I descended the laundry stone and sprinted inside to telephone Glynis. Her line was busy. I tried again. Still busy.

I began to run back outside and bumped into Glynis on the backyard steps.

"She's in my house." Glynis was biting her lips.

"I know," I moaned. "I saw her coming up the hill."

"She's talking to my mother."

"What's she saying?"

"I don't know."

"Go and listen," I said.

"Oh no, I'm afraid. You go and listen."

"Oh no. It's your house. You go and listen"

Mrs. Coker had challenged the class several weeks into the term.

173

"Go ask any of the girls who passed through me." She wagged her finger. "I do not care if you live in Timbuktu—I will visit your home." I didn't believe her. None of us did.

"I'm never satisfied merely seeing a parent's signature on report cards."

I dismissed her. How would a grandmother who lives in the West End ever make the grueling journey to Upper Patton Street in the East End?

This was before my mind had circled back to Trinity School days when Attatie was meeting with my Class Seven teacher. An uneasy feeling strangled me for the length of that meeting as I watched the two women standing on the corridor, Attatie in wrapper and head tie, Mrs. Longstretch in her short dress and stretched hair. I remember hoping they were not speaking English. My mother spoke laughable English, and I was afraid it would rub off on me.

I did wonder, after Mrs. Coker's challenge, what would happen if she met my mother. Would she insist on a conversation in English? Would Mrs. Coker come down to speaking Krio?

I had the feeling Mrs. Collier would do something like that—peak in Krio, or attempt whatever language my mother spoke. But would Mrs. Coker do that? Has she ever spoken Krio in her life?

I knew for certain that she did not speak my mother's Soso tongue, or any other tribal language.

When the days and weeks passed, and Mrs. Coker didn't come, I slipped into relief and stopped dusting and worrying. Yes, I used to dust the bookcase and the pictures on the wall every day after school, especially the one of Papa in his Prince of Wales old-boy uniform.

"What am I going to do?" Glynis was wringing her fingers uncontrollably.

"She's going to tell your mother about the low marks you've been getting in every subject."

Of course, I wasn't being helping. But Mrs. Coker was in the neighborhood; it was every girl for herself.

"Why did she come all this way?" Glynis whined.

"How would I know?"

"She's come to destroy us."

"And she's coming to my house next."

"I'll never be able to ask my mother for anything again, ever in my life, until the day I die." Glynis wept.

She went back and forth, peeping through the garage gate. I went up and down on the laundry stone, careful not to pull my head up too high over the wall.

"What's she still doing in my house?" Glynis said.

"She has a lot to say about you."

I had no worries about what Mrs. Coker might say about me. My marks were good then, and my experience with Trinity School teachers had taught me to remain quiet, in the background. What I was most concerned about was the imminent collision of my home and school lives. My Trinity School teachers had never ever expressed the desire to know who my parents were, or where I lived, let alone come to my house and meet them. It was a mixed blessing. On the one hand, none of them, except for Mrs. Longstretch, had to meet my mother. On the other hand, I had to remain a nobody throughout elementary school. This time, my schoolteacher—a secondary school teacher, at that— was coming to my house.

I had one thing to be thankful for.

Attatie was not home.

Papa will speak to her in English, thank God. She will see his Prince Walean picture and know he went to a *good* school. She will see volumes of Encyclopedia Britannica in the living room bookcase. She will see the classics like *Alice in Wonderland* and *The Lion, the Witch, and the Wardrobe*. She will see Papa's favorites books, such as *Not Yet Uhuru*, and *A History of West Africa*.

"There she is!" Glynis screamed, her forehead still glued to the garage door.

"Is she coming toward my house?" It was my turn to crush my fingers.

"Should I go home now and face my mother?"

I did not answer. I had my own problems.

"My name is Florence Coker," she told Papa in a polite tone. "I am Memuna's Form teacher."

They shook hands, and Papa and I ushered Mrs. Coker through the front door as if she was a dignitary. She was constantly wiping sweat beads off her face, but her shoulders stood upright, and her eyes—those resolute eyes—said I can do plenty more.

We reached a perfect spot—the hallway where we usually held family prayers. Papa pointed Mrs. Coker to the parlor. She turned right to enter it, raised her head ever so slightly, and *bang!* A cheerful young man posing in a white suit and bowler hat -- the darting lion of the Prince Walean crest forming a straight line from the hatband to the breast pocket.

Mrs. Coker's smile put me back in the classroom at Trinity School. It erased the pain of Ms. Jackson's complaints about too many non-Christians in the school. It erased my vomit on Trinity Church's aisle, the bullying from Mary Bull, and even the woman who complained about the suppression of legacy admissions.

It didn't matter that Glynis had gone when I left Papa and Mrs. Coker to talk and returned to the backyard. I sat on the laundry stone alone and replayed in my mind the image of Mrs. Coker looking at Papa's old-boy picture. Her softened eyes and gathered lips. That indulgent smile she displayed whenever her class pupils scored high marks.

My home and school life were merging, in more ways than one.

***

I found out after she left that Mrs. Coker had told Papa what he already knew about me."

"What's that?" I said.

"You're never with the others in class."

"What?"

You're always away."

"But where would I go? I'm always in class. Ask Glynis. I'm always in class."

Papa did not respond, but he was not reproachful either.

Though, even as I tried to dispute Mrs. Coker's complaint, I sensed the place to which she was referring. It was the place I went when my grand-uncles said I was wrong to complain about Mohammed stealing meat from my rice. The place I hid when I could not tell Miss Jackson that in spite of my religion, I, too, was a worthy child. The place I retreated to when I couldn't fight Annie Brown, and when I couldn't tell Attatie I had had enough of her offerings. It was a world in which I was beginning to feel comfortable, but I had no words with which to describe it.

The Thing

The Leah Street house had witches, too. This time, it was Granny who sent a man to flush them out. The man came with a clothlike thing of brownish black, red, and white, decorated with cowrie shells. It was attached to a string, like a pet, that jumped around with a pull of the string. It looked like it had been dipped in palm oil.

The man sat next to the thing in the middle of the parlor. He wore a joyless face and an old mud cloth shirt that exposed his naked sidebones. He held a whip in his hand. Not the kind used to cane children, but a thicker rod covered in leather.

Papa, Attatie, Granny Kadi, me, Mohammed, and my three sisters all sat on a reem mat, the way we did with sacrifices and prayers.

"Is this everybody that lives in this house?" the man asked Papa.

"This is everybody," Papa replied.

The man then lifted the whip up high and made a gentle landing on *the thing*, as though afraid of upsetting it. He repeated the move several times, each time murmuring something to himself. It appeared he was talking to the thing, because he raised his head a few moments later and told Papa that a witch had transformed itself into one of the adults living in the house. Its purpose, the witch flusher suspected, was to destroy Papa's children. Therefore, every adult in the house had to take hold of the whip and prove him or herself a non-witch.

"Sassa," Papa said to the thing, and held the whip high up, imitating the way the witch flusher did earlier. "I'm the father of these children. If I turn against them in any way, do anything to prevent them from becoming somebody tomorrow. Then Sassa, do not exclude me from your wrath." He turned to the man to say *I'm done*, then replaced the whip on Sassa.

It was Attatie's turn.

"Siminie Conteh, Karimu Sillah, Mameh Sillah," she said. "You have been my helpers in my marital home and with these children since the birth of Mohammed, up to the last one here, Hassana." She paused and tucked in her wrapper between her legs. "If, whether inadvertently or deliberately, I have done anything to harm my own children, do not exclude me from your wrath." She returned the whip to Sassa.

There was an uneasy moment during which Sassa's owner fixed his gaze on Papa, and Papa fixed his on Attatie, who looked back to Papa.

Papa broke the impasse. "Granny Kadi, do you have anything to say?"

Granny Kadi chuckled. "Oh, what do I have to say? These children are as much mine as they are yours. Anyone harming them is only harming me. They are the reason I have the privilege of staying here."

"Still, you must have something in mind," Attatie said. "This is an opportunity to clear your chest."

Granny Kadi picked up the whip and informed Sassa that she was one of the inhabitants of the house, well-taken-care-of and regarded as a family member. She asked it to guide and protect us all from evil spirits and witches.

***

For the entire month that Granny Kadi was at Connaught Hospital, Attatie got up before the fowls and shouted out chores that everyone must do before leaving for school.

"Mohammed, make sure the water drum is full. Amie, I don't want to see a single dirty dish in the kitchen. Mameh, get out the mortar and pestle. Abassy, make sure all the pots are clean and ready for me."

The houseboy had to be split wood and get the kitchen fire going. Most importantly, the noisy activities like pounding on the mortar and the washing pots and pans had to be carried out under the window of the bedroom where Papa was still sleeping. It was from the same spot that she screamed commands.

After we left for school, and Papa for work, Attatie stayed behind to cook. Ever since I can remember, she had committed herself to sending Granny a bowl of soup every day, to eat with her *agidie*. She made sure Granny received her soup before going to open her store, then she closed it early to go help Granny Kadi's daughter at the hospital. Papa left work early and picked us up from school. Mohammed preferred to make his own way home. We ate together, then cleared the dining table and settled down to homework, while Papa continued his office work from home.

As the weeks went by, Attatie returned later and later every day from the hospital. Usually, Fatmata and Hassana were already in bed, and Mohammed, Amie, and I were in the living room watching television with Papa. Then one day, she returned around midnight, Granny Kadi's daughter in tow, together with the former Soso dancer who was Granny Kadi's friend. Attatie whispered something into Papa's ears, and Papa got up and turned off the TV. The women went into Granny Kadi's bedroom, and before I could ask Papa why he turned off the TV, the daughter's wailing had enveloped the house, and Attatie was sending Mohammed to the upstairs storage room to fetch the white window curtains.

* * *

Granny Kadi's daughter stayed in her bedroom past the 40th Day funeral rites. Attatie told us she was taking a break from her alcoholic husband. She got up early and helped with the cooking so that Attatie was able to open the store before lunchtime, and since she no longer went to the hospital, resumed normal closing hours.

Mohammed, Amie, and I got off our individual buses at Goderich Street. By arrangement with some parents picking up their daughters from St. Joseph's Convent and FSSG, Fatmata and Hassana were dropped at the store. We changed from our uniforms in a small cubicle at the back, then ate whatever cassava leaves or potato leaves had been brought to the store. Then we did our homework before coming out to help with customers.

This schedule continued until we marked Granny Kadi's one-year memorial with the usual *sara* prayers, accompanied by food and drinks with friends and relatives. Then the daughter returned to her alcoholic husband.

One of Attatie's aunties from Sackville Street began coming every morning to help with the cooking. Grandma Ndamba told us, with scorn in her voice, that Granny Kadi's daughter left because "your grandmother at Boyle Street" didn't want her living in our house. She also said our relatives at Boyle Street had killed off Granny Kadi with a *sassa* because they didn't want Attatie's rice business to prosper.

Then, a few weeks later, one of Attatie's distant cousins also came to help. Aunty Mbalia told us that Papa had fathered a child while he was working in the provinces, and the Boyle Street family had accepted and named the child.

Before long, Grandma Ndamba occupied Granny Kadi's room, and Aunty Mbalia came every morning to help her with the cooking and other housework. Attatie resumed a schedule that was even more hectic than before. She left with our change of clothes before any of us were up, and at closing time, she put us in a taxi home and continued about her rice business.

The New School

"What does it say?"

She stood behind me on the storefront of a three-story building, pressing her hands on my shoulders.

"Stand here and read it to me."

Attatie was always asking me to read things to her. That was what bonded the two of us closer than any of my siblings. I loved to read.

I raised an eager thirteen-year-old head up to the white letters against a black background of the store's wooden sign. They were as bold as her actions.

Aminata Sillah, Trader, 45 Goderich Street, Freetown.

"You see that?" She whisked me around to face her. "If I can do all this without going to school, imagine what you can do if you keep your books open."

The store quickly became my second home, and a second school.

Other than adult family and friends of my parents, I had been raised to distrust strangers. There were always stories, when I was little, of demons hauling away little children. Once, when we were in infant school, we had to wear red strips of cloth on our wrists to wade away a particular demon that was hanging around looking to abduct little children. At another time, we made a X with charcoal on our foreheads to scare away another that also came looking for children.

At the store, I could interact freely with complete strangers.

"How much is the rice?" a customer asked one Saturday, staring at the height of the stuffed thirty-pound bags.

Attatie had brought an exercise book and made me write the prices in it, in case we forgot them.

"Get out your store book," she would say, as soon as a customer walked in. When the prices changed, she made sure we tore off the pages of the old prices, wrote down the new ones, and repeated them to her several times.

I didn't have to consult the book this time. I pointed around the store.

"Fifty leones for a bag of Wala rice. Thirty leones a bag for the white rice. Twenty leones, fifty cents for the Burma rice. And twenty-five leones for each box of Aunt Carolina and Uncle Bens."

"Where's the tester?" the woman said.

I followed her around the store as she injected the tip of the metal tester into one sisal bag after another. She poured the sample grains into her palm, then used the tester tip to dissect the grains and examine each one's individual character, the wholeness of its shape, its uniformity with the group, the clarity of its eyes, before bringing her hand to her nose.

"It doesn't smell," I said.

She ignored me and kept the grains to her nose a while longer, before emptying her hands as though she was dropping dirt on the floor. She went on to test another bag, and another bag, from top to bottom, putting the grains in her palm, dissecting them, and still smelling them. Then she wanted to know how long the rice had been sitting in the store, and the country of origin of the white rice. Before I could finish answering her questions, she put the tester back into my hand and turned to leave.

"Why did you thrust the tester into so many bags if you knew you weren't going to buy anything!" I shouted to her back.

"Isn't that the reason you have a store?" she snapped. "So that everybody can come in and look for what they want?"

"No," I snapped back. "You come in to buy."

"If I don't see a bag of rice with eyes that I like, I will not buy. It's my money."

"Never mind, *kombra*," Attatie said, appealing to the customer's maternal indulgence. "It's all right. Maybe you will come and buy from us next time."

"This is the dry season," Attatie said to me, after the customer left. "You must be patient with customers. There is newly harvested rice everywhere."

Then she called one of the laborers who usually wait outside the store for work, to go check what other stores on Goderich Street were selling for. When the laborer returned and said one of the stores was selling the Wala brand about five leones less than we were, Attatie said, "Get your store book and make a change in the price."

Still, she spent the rest of the day putting down what she called amateur rice traders who did not know how to set prices.

***

Another Saturday, a woman came into the store and did the same thing. I could tell from the way her wrapper mismatched her blouse, and the way she tied her wrapper on top of the blouse, that she was a market woman who sold rice and maybe other things, like sugar and flour.

I watched her with clenched teeth as she thrust the iron tester into almost every bag, separated the grains in her palms, brought them to her nose, and then let the grains fall to the ground. Through it all, I mirrored my mother and remained quiet.

When the woman was completely satisfied, she turned to Attatie.

"Where's the laborer?"

It was a quiet day, so the few laborers who hung around in the morning had left to look for work elsewhere.

"Which bag do you want?" Attatie asked her.

I couldn't believe where her gaze went. Right down to the bottom of a row of ten fifty-pound bags.

"You mean you couldn't find a bag of rice with clear eyes on the top rows?" I couldn't help myself.

She turned and gave me a stormy look.

"That's all right, *kombra*," Attatie said. "We can get that one just for you, because I know you will be my customer from now on." Then she turned to Mohammed. "Go up the road and fetch two strong laborers."

"Is it forty leones a bag?" the woman said

It was fifty leones per bag, but Attatie had said we could reduce the price to forty-five at the lowest.

"Forty-five-fifty," Attatie replied, just for you.

The woman pulled back a bit and scratched her head.

"You can have it for forty-five leones," I said, trying to show that I had learn how to appease a customer.

It was the dry season, after all, and five hundred leones was usually the most we took in on any one day. I didn't want Attatie to lose the sale.

Attatie feigned hesitation, then nodded. The woman untied a knot at the top edge of her wrapper and pulled out a large bundle of soiled notes. She counted fifty leones into my hand. I put the bills inside the covered dish and picked up five ten-cent coins.

They started from the top row. Each laborer held two ends of a bag and carried it like a dead body, down to the ground. This way, they pulled down every bag until they reached the tenth bag—the one that started the pile, the customer's choice. They pulled it out, then started the task of replacing all the bags.

"Where am I taking you to?" said one of the laborers.

"Fireburn," the woman said.

"Two leones."

"Kortor!" the woman screamed. "You're asking me for two leones just to go around the corner?"

"But this bag is heavy, and Fireburn is not around the corner."

The woman bent down and picked up an end portion of the bag and began pulling it up.

"Is this what you call a heavy bag? I can carry this myself, but for the distance."

The laborer chuckled.

"I'm not paying you two leones to carry one bag of rice to Fireburn."

"OK. One-seventy-five."

"One pound."

"One-fifty."

"One-twenty-five."

"I'm only doing this because you are a woman. If I was dealing with a man—"

"Kortor, pick the bag up and let's go," she snapped. "I have work to do."

The other laborer gazed from Attatie to the rice bags and back again.

"Give him fifty cents," Attatie said, and I opened the enameled steel dish we used as a cash register.

***

We got back at the retail customers during the rainy season. In the months of July and August especially, when even rice farmers ate cassava, customers begged us to sell them a bag or two. Atatie preferred dealing with those mostly male up-country customers who arrived in muscular lorries.

"How many bags do you need?" Attatie's was taking in the lorry packed in front of the store.

The two men who had exited it looked weary from the trip, their bloodshot eyes and rumpled cardigans a contrast with the smart leather briefcase one of them carried.

"Two hundred and fifty bags," the man with the briefcase answered.

Attatie quoted a wholesale price of forty-two leones per bag, and the bargaining started -- the men lowered the price by two leones, Attatie raised it up a leone and fifty cents. They went back and forth like that, Attatie blaming the high cost-price set by the Trade Board, and the men, the high cost of transportation, for eating into their respective profit margins. Finally, they agreed on a price of forty leones and twenty-five cents.

"Get the shop book," Attatie called to me.

The men moved to the far side of the store to think out their calculations. Upcountry traders were usually not men who could read and write.

Attatie gave me a pencil. "Calculate one hundred bags at forty leones each."

I got the exercise book on whose cover she had instructed me to write *store book* and did my arithmetic. I wrote down four thousand leones.

She turned the book to face her, squinted her eyes on the page, and then said, "O.K. Now, four thousand leones in two places. What does that make?"

By the time I finished writing down eight thousand, the customers had finished thinking their calculations; they were already removing large bundles of money from the briefcase and spreading them on a table next to the second entrance to the store.

"Now, for the fifty bags, calculate forty leones for each bag, Attatie said.

I wrote two thousand leones under the eight thousand figure.

"What's the total we have so far?" she said.

"Ten thousand," I replied.

The men had finished laying out their bills; they now stood over us, arms folded over their rumpled cardigans.

"My children are my clerks," Attatie said, then returned to me. "Now, let's calculate the twenty-five cents, two hundred and fifty times."

Numbers that do not end with zeros were nightmares for me. "Why don't' we take off the 25 cents," I said. "They've come all the way from the provinces."

"Good idea." One of the men laughed.

"Yes, we have come all the way from Kono," said the other. "We traveled all night. Have sympathy for our rumpled clothes."

"Let's see how many school shoes twenty-five cents in two-hun-dred-and-fifty places will buy," Attatie said.

The lesson in patience was sinking in. Unlike school, where I could simply put down a wrong answer and wait for the teacher's red mark on my book, this was life, with consequences. I was going to need uni-form, shoes, and books when school reopened in September.

"Twenty-five cents in four places," she repeated.

I turned to the book's back cover; it had no multiplication table.

"It's not written in the book," Attatie said. "Not everything is go-ing to be written in a book for you. Some things must come from your head. Think! Open your head and think."

That was easy for her to say. She could not read and write, so her head was used to processing gigabytes of information every day. She was fond of repeated what she said was her grandfather's saying that there was the idea first, then the book, and not the other way around.

For now, she gave up on me and asked if the customers were ready with payment.

The men pointed to the table with the money. We moved over to count stacks of one thousand leones until we got ten thousand. Then the arithmetic lesson resumed.

"If twenty-five cents a bag equals five leones for twenty bags, then how many leones is two hundred and fifty bags."

I'd always thought word problems were only for school. I was wondering how many of my classmates were stuck solving word problems in the middle of the long holidays. Most of my friends were either sitting at home listening to music or hanging around in the middle of town, going in and out of shops just for the heck of it.

"Turn to a clean page on the book." Attatie brought me back. "Write down 'twenty bags equals five leones,' twelve times."

Happy to not engage my mind in any more thinking, I wrote as she instructed: two columns, five lines each of 20 equals 5, and a third column with two lines. Then as instructed, I added the bags columns to get a total of 240, and the Le5 columns for a total of Le60.

"Now," she said, "let's see how much the remaining ten bags cost at 25cents each."

That was easy. I wrote down Le2.50, then added Le 2.50 and Le 60 and Le10,000 and

shouted jubilantly, Le10,062.50.

Attatie's three years of school, and probably, none at all, in the case of upcountry traders, they could conduct business that involved calculating large amounts of money without the use of paper, pencil or a calculator. How is it that Attatie was able to engage, so naturally, in price warfare, customer satisfaction, advertisement, and accounting for her business. The market women and the laborers did not go to school either, but they conducted business negotiations on which their livelihood depended.

Hawa and Mafula

The store did keep my siblings and I out of trouble during the long holidays. Not that I yearned to be out of trouble, despite Attatie's threats. It was disheartening to stand in front of our gate in the evenings and hear Glynis and Melisa talk about the latest happenings in the neighborhood, or the boys they met while strolling downtown.

But at the store, it was the Kamara sisters who painted me several colors with envy. Hawa and Mafula lived at the last house on Lumley Street before the road runs into a tributary of Bambara Spring. Theirs was a small tin house at the back of the larger wood house owned by relatives of ours, the Baratay family.

Hawa had gone to FSSG, and Mafula to YWCA school, but being at the store enabled us to maintain the acquaintances developed at Trinity School. The summer after our second year in secondary school, I started to notice a change in the reserved, bookish girl the Trinity School headmistress once begged to adopt. Hawa's soft voice was disappearing, as was the dainty way she often folded her arms when she spoke. Now, she gesticulated the same jagged way Mafula did, scattering her arms up in the air. She also dressed like Mafula, with large earrings, halter tops, even lipstick. Of course, I envied the change in Hawa, though Attatie would frown when she came to the store, and after she left, would repeat one of the problem she had with native parents—that they allowed their school-age children to go out dressed like adults."

Attatie could not wrap her mind around the reason their mother did not take Hawa and Mafula with her to sell pepper at the market during the long holidays.

"Country mothers don't know how to raise girls," she would say, as Hawa and Mafula strolled up and down Goderich Street, jesting with the neighborhood boys.

Then, during our third year of secondary school, Hawa came by the store one Saturday afternoon, when Attatie was home cooking. She was coming from the hairdresser's, her hair shining with fresh curls. She held a half-jar of hair cream.

"We're going to a summer picnic at Lumley Beach," she said, explaining the curls.

Maybe it was to camouflage my envy that I dipped a playful finger into the hair cream and rubbed on the skin between my braids. The only time my hair was stretched and curled was for Eid-ul-Fitr prayers.

"We're going to be late." Mafula arrived behind her sister.

She was wearing an halter top and pencil skirt that squeezed her manly hips. She had red lipstick, a pancaked face, and plenty of eyeshadow. I was grateful Attatie was not around.

"That's the top I was going to wear." Hawa pointed to Mafula.

Mafula responded with a short, thoughtful look at her older sister, then said, "You can wear the mini-dress. You look good in it."

She motioned for Hawa to hurry on, and soon, the sisters had their backs to me.

Less than an hour later, Attatie arrived at the store. We were preparing to eat *foofoo* and *orbiata* when Aunty Mbalu Baratay came rushing down the short cement steps that separated Lumley Street from Goderich Street. She stood on the Goderich Street landing and tried to flag down a taxi, holding her head tie.

"Where're you going in such a hurry?" Attatie called to her.

She came running.

"What is it? Attatie saw the confusion in her face.

"The Temne woman staying in the adjoining behind us…" Aunty Mbalu said, hands trembling as she tied her head.

"What happened to her?" Attatie said.

Aunty Mbalu finished tying her head and turned her arms inside out to express hopelessness.

"We just heard that her daughters got into a road accident at Lumley Beach Road."

Attatie turned to face me, as if to shield me from Aunty Mbalu's words. In return, I pressed all ten fingers on the hair cream between my braids.

"They said they were in a car driven by one of the neighborhood boys, speeding on the Lumley Beach Road."

I remember thinking that their mother should have allowed Mrs. Kissling to adopt Hawa. She would have received the kind of handling Attatie believed only people born and raised in Freetown know how to inflict on children. Their mother would not have lost two daughters in a joyride accident on the same day.

Wasted Tears

Glynis, Melissa, and I were now great buddies. Melissa joined Glynis and I at the corner of Leah Street and Vinton Streets for the walk to Clock Tower, where we fought to get on a bus. Then, on those days when Papa didn't pick us up from school, we walked to the Congo Cross bus stop and fought to get on a bus for Clock Tower.

We were standing at the mouth of Annie Walsh School's driveway, waiting for the snake of cars to go by, when I said, "I don't believe I once died to come to Annie Walsh School."

"Why didn't you go there?" Melissa asked.

Glynis let out a loud sigh. "Don't you know Mrs. Forster?"

Of course, I was familiar with Mrs. Forster's haughty tantrum, but I didn't know what Glynis had revealed that afternoon—that the family members of an aggrieved student from Fourah Bay had once walked right into Mrs. Forster's office, threw obscene language at her, and even called her a harlot. Obviously, I was not from Fourah Bay, even though I had the kind of Marabou name any girl from Fourah Bah would carry. But from my own experiences with other tribes, I was beginning to realize the wide gaps that existed amongst us. I was not yet able to analyze Mrs. Foster's ignorance about the country in which she was raised, nor was I even able to contextualize my own. I simply knew and accepted the fact that her resentment of anyone with a non-British name was becoming of the society in which I was growing up.

***

It was always exciting meeting those elementary school friends with whom you did not move to the same secondary school. You grin at each other, reminisce about elementary school days, catch up on news about other former classmates, then share news on each other's new life at their respective secondary schools.

"Do you know what happened to Joy?" Fredericka brought her mouth to my ear as though the street traders and passerbys on Kissy Road would want to eavesdrop on what happened to Joy.

"No. What happened to her?" I said.

"She's not at Annie Walsh School anymore."

"Why?"

"She stopped coming."

"She died?"

Fredericka pulled back, then returned to my ear. "Her parents sent her to the provinces."

I didn't know Joy Decker had relatives in the provinces. Her name certainly did not reveal that. Girls who go to school in the provinces usually had family members there they stayed with. Did she have relative there?

I always thought Joy was like me, unfamiliar with up-country. My only visit to the provinces was on the healing trip once, when I was too young to remember much. My only lasting memory were the mud huts and thatched roofs, the thinly clothed kwashiorkor children in torn panties, their exposed bodies powdered with dust. They were the picture of what I'd come to know as country people, provincial life, and I wasn't able to picture Joy Decker in their midst.

"Why did her parents send her to the provinces?" I opened my eyes wide.

Fredericka returned her mouth to my ear. "She got pregnant."

I looked for signs in Fredericka's eyes that said she was joking, but she bit her lower lip and fanned her head.

When I heard, a few months later, that Barbara had moved out of the Parson's house and stopped attending Annie Walsh School, for reasons no one knew, I wished I could take back those tears I wasted at the Trinity School compound.

Eid Lunch

A t Kissy Road, Papa and his six children turned into Lower Patton Street, and Attatie took Upper Patton Street. We were coming from Eid-ul-Fitr prayers.

It was a family tradition. Even those who had married into far-away families went to Granny's house after Eid prayers. All of Momodu Wullays descendants, as she called us, brought blessings from Eid prayer to her house. She welcomed us in ancient jewelry and new clothes. Even moved her arthritic legs as she beamed on a morris chair.

The children sat around Granny's morris chair and at from large bowls. The grandchildren sat on reed mats to eat. Girls and boys separated in groups of three or four around a bowl of rice and fish stew. As we grabbed mounds of rice and licked our fingers, it was a time to catch up on who was not allowed to go to Eid prayers because of bad behavior, or because a parent had no money for clothes. Throughout the lunch, we cautioned one whose *sari* was getting too close to the food bowl, or another whose food was falling on her satin blouse.

We finished eating, lined up under the apple tree, and straddled our legs as Aminata poured soapy water from a calabash to wash our hands. Regardless of the number of times I washed my hands, the fragrance of granny's Prayday stew always lingered for the rest of the day.

Attatie had already changed out of her taffeta ensemble when we got home, her jewelry now accessorizing a crepe outfit.

"I'm expecting a lot of people this evening," she said to me, from the outside kitchen threshold, where she was supervising the houseboy and some other women she had hired for the day.

Before my sisters and I had finished changing from our *saris*, a young man came from the Piknis of Goree Street with a large bowl of vegetable salad, Mammy Penina's daughter sent two loaves of pound cake, Aunty Marion sent rice bread and peppered chicken.

I went around the house, sniffing the fish stew from Granny's lunch, following instructions to bring down plates and cutlery from the storage room, or arranging drinking glasses on the table. In the afternoon, the guests began to arrive, all of them Christians. Ginger beer, soft drinks, and alcohol were served with the jollof rice, peppered chicken, roast beef, salad, Scotch eggs, cake, and rice bread.

Some of our cousins from Boyle Street, Goree Street, and Jenkins Street came by. We took over the downstairs parlor, ate and danced to songs blasting from Papa's gramophone.

Throughout the evening, my mind kept circling back to the lunch at Granny's house. Other than one or two of my cousins who casually said, "Where's Attatie?" and moved on to other conversations, all the adults at Granny's house gave their mouths kola nut.

The Vice President's Lodge

Some of the places Attatie went after she closed her store and put us in a taxi were the homes of those politicians, alongside whom she had fought during the budding days of the APC Party. She took me in a taxicab with her one Friday to visit the vice president's wife.

"We don't know if she's in," said the fatigued soldier who greeted us at the security station.

He was as thin as his rifle. He had tucked his head inside of the taxi to talk.

Attatie swelled up and tightened her lips. The soldier frowned and returned to the security cubicle. An elderly one replaced him.

"Good evening, Ma," he said in a jovial tone.

"Do you want to say you people don't know me, Mrs. Aminata Sillah?" Attatie said.

"We know you very well, ma." The soldier smiled.

"OK. Go tell Missus Koroma her sister is here."

A new guard walked us to a large, white-washed building. We entered through a room that looked like a police station, with only a worn-out couch and a few enamel chairs. Men in security uniforms merged with plain clothes men in small group conversations. Then we passed through a corridor where another group of men were talking with grand gesticulations.

"This is Mister Sesay." Attatie pointed to one in a half kaftan-like *rappel* shirt. "We used to attend APC rallies together."

Mr. Sesay gave me a hearty smile and a vigorous handshake. Then he introduced Attatie to the others as one of the founding members of the APC Party. There was a ten-minute reminiscence of *the old party days*, before we were ushered into a spacious lounge with more uniformed and plain-clothes men. Above their heads, a composed President Stevens guarded his place on the wall. I don't know what I was expecting, but the room was almost as bare as the security station, with two velvet settees and a rug that could have been in the house of a mid-level civil servant. There was also a dining table with several chairs around it, one with a broken leg.

Our guide took us up two sets of tiled staircases, into a sitting room with plush leather settees and gold-rimmed pictures of President Stevens. In the middle of a large sectional, looking like a patient in a hospital ward, the vice president was planked by clean-shaven men in black suits and tailored safaris.

"Missus Aminata Sillah," the vice president hailed, in a hoarse voice, then made an enormous effort to lean off the couch and give Attatie a jolly handshake. "How's Mami doing."

Attatie said Papa was doing fine. Then, with Attatie's hand still in his, he addressed the men around him.

"You see this woman here." His free hand moved feebly across the room.

Every gaze froze on Attatie.

"This is a party stalwart. She is one of the women who helped us fight when we were in the opposition."

The nods were heavy, the grins serious.

"In the early days when we faced challenges," he took a laborious breath, his hand hanging in the air in front of him, "it was women like these that helped us hold onto Freetown's East End."

The nods became bows, and the grins widened as the VP explained that Attatie was also the niece to Morlai Sillah of Central I. The men introduced themselves—director of this bank, permanent secretary of that ministry, president of that board. She said she knew some of them, and others she recognized from newspapers and television.

"Remember their names," she whispered in my ear.

I nodded and tried as best I could to keep the names in my mind, but by the time we got up to leave, I could only remember the permanent secretary of trade, mostly because I'd already heard Attatie drop his name during conversations at the store.

"I just stopped by to see my sister," Attatie said to the VP, who now let go of her hand and took mine.

His grip felt like my hand was in a jar of cotton wool.

"Your mother is a strong woman." He pointed his free hand toward Attatie.

As we turned to leave, I nodded shyly and said goodbye.

Several women in floral blouses and wrappers surrounded Mrs. Koroma. Some had their head ties sprawled on the couch next to them. Others had their slippers sitting next to their bare feet on the rug. A heavy woman laid on one of the settees, her head on the lap of another. Another woman had her hand in a palm oil sauce she was eating from a deep bowl. The coffee table held two dishes with serving spoons surging out of their covers. On the settee next to Mrs. Koroma was a woman in a black dress, with broad shoulders and sunken eyes—the only woman without a head tie or wrapper. Her hair was straightened and held back in a short ponytail. At the far end of the room, a grandmother was dozing off on a morris chair.

"Let us eat." The woman with the bowl motioned a palm-oil-coated hand to Attatie.

Attatie returned the obligation with a corresponding thank you and moved to greet Mrs. Koroma. She was either ready for bed, or had not changed out of her nightie at all that day. A head tie of the same cloth as her cotton wrapper hung loosely over her braids.

"This is Mister Sillah's replica!" Mrs. Koroma caressed my chin.

"You should see her older sister." Attatie took a seat between Mrs. Koroma and the woman in the black dress.

Before she did so, she appeared to lock eyes with the woman.

When we got home, Attatie collected Mohammed, Amie, Fatmata, Abassy, and Hassana into the living room.

"Sit down," she said.

Of course, everyone, including me, wondered who was in trouble. Abassy looked resigned to his punishment, and Mohammed already had the I-didn't-do-it look on his face. But Attatie had other things on her mind.

"Tell them." She crossed a finger from me to my siblings. "Tell them what the vice president said about me."

***

A few days before our visit to the VP's house, I was watching the evening news with Attatie and Papa when Mrs. Koroma came on. She was visiting a children's hospital somewhere in the provinces. "Her head tie should say her husband is Vice President of the country," Attatie said forcefully, not a sorcerer."

Mrs. Koroma was wearing a tie-dye gown with her matching head tie. Standing to her right was a woman in a plain, sleeveless frock; the same woman we met later, sitting on the couch with Mrs. Koroma. "Is there no woman of understanding around her?" Attatie complained.

"The head tie looks fine to me," Papa countered, and with that, dragged a smoking stick into an arid bush.

"What does a Krio woman know about head ties? Where was she when we were being beaten up by soldiers?"

Papa shut up.

But it was clear, even to me, that the bush burned on in Attatie's mind. *Who knows where I would have been today, had that delegation from Boyle Street not pooped on my dreams? What other Marabou woman would have been better suited to put the wife of the Vice President's wardrobe up to city standards? Who better to dress her up, every day, in broad eyed lace gowns, taffetas and brocades, and blow-up head ties that assert her husband's position?*
***

Osora School was named after the wife of a former British missionary, but by the time Hassana started Class One, it was called The Freetown Secondary School for Girls. Hassana made instant friendship at FSSG with a girl named Elizabeth. She came home from school every day and rushed to the telephone after eating. They kept the lines busy for hours, leaving the receiver off the hook for a long drink of water or a snack, then returning to talk some more.

Papa brought Hassana home from school one day to say he'd finally met Elizabeth—skinny like Hassana, and equally talkative. To Attatie's question about Elizabeth's family, Papa had no answer. We continued putting up with *Elizabeth did this and Elizabeth did that*, until Prayday.

A uniformed chauffeur parked in front of our house after we had just returned from prayers.

Hassana recognized him. "That's Elizabeth's driver."

He carried a large, covered tray of food into the house and asked for Mrs. Sillah. The tray of food was from Mrs. Taylor, the driver said, to wish Mrs. Sillah and family a happy Eid Day.

Mrs. Taylor's dishes were added to the several bowls of Prayday meals we received from Attatie's Christian friends, and soon, she and her husband were regulars at our Prayday parties.

Attatie still made comments, in front of the television, on what she considered Mrs. Taylor's lackluster performance as Mrs. Koroma's righthand woman, but she did so mostly in friendly humor that Papa was happy to indulge in.

The New Neighbors

Unlike our Goree Street neighbors, whose lifestyles we copied, neighbors who babysat us from their windows, the Leah Street neighbors sent us hunkering down behind closed windows. The Idris family, especially, were not *good* people. The parents and their five children lived in a small tin house without electricity or running water. Yanoh, the eldest of the Idris children, came running out of their hut one Sunday morning, throwing her hands up in the air.

"You double, triple bastard."

"You harlot!" her boyfriend shot back. "Every man in this town has been inside your knickers."

"You street boy. Your penis cannot satisfy even a twice-mutilated woman."

"You don't wash your panties. Who'll marry a woman like you?"

"You'll drink your fucking mother in a whiskey bottle. Who wants a man like you?"

God knows we were expecting *good* company. The director of Trade Board and his family were coming for breakfast after church.

"Close the windows." Attatie came running downstairs with orders.

"You—didn't I tell you to sweep the living room? And you—why are there still dirty dishes on the dining table? You! Get out the beef from the fridge."

There was no escaping the noise from the gathering crowd outside, though. Even Attatie was aware that we had landed in deep dirt.

When we first moved to Leah Street, I thought the boney-faced, lanky girl with a teasing smile was a pupil in Form Four or Five. Within weeks, I found out that Yanoh was the mother of the runny-nosed toddler often trudging through the dirt yard, as well as the little boy who wore the brown khaki of a municipal elementary school.

When her four younger siblings and her son were at school, Yanoh left the child with her mother, a beefy woman who spoke mostly in Temne, at the top of her voice to peddle the family's merchandise *du saison*—mangoes, corn, groundnuts during the rainy season, and oranges and bananas during the dry season. When her siblings returned from school, they, too, put trays on their heads and took to the streets, hawking fruits in their school uniforms. Bockarie, the eldest son, seldom did any of the trading. He simply walked around with muscular elbows, looking like an angry boxer.

One Ramadan, Yanoh started her own business. She sold oranges for her mother during the day, and in the evening, she fried fish, *akara*, plantains, and potatoes, which she sold under a tin lamp in front of their gate. Her food became part of my *ifta* meal. My siblings also, and even Papa, sometimes patronized her, while Attatie would watch us eat her food as though we were chewing snake liver.

The Idris family patriarch was already gray and stooping when we moved to Leah Street. He was some sort of tribal judge. His busiest days were Sundays, when crowds spilled onto the street, speaking in hastened Temne. From our dining room window, I would watch a husband and wife arguing in front of him, or a father pointing at an impudent son. The small boulders scattered over their yard supplemented the shaky wooden benches on which litigants sat. As each family's case was heard, they took their time moving on, greeting familiar faces, or in some cases, complaining to those who would listen, about Pa Idris's judgment.

Even when there were no cases to be heard, people stopped by to sit and draw wisdom from Pa Idris. Sometimes they brought sheep, fowl, bags of rice, beans, and cassava, as thank you payment for the cases he adjudicated. The litigants were also clients of the Idris matriarch's food business.

Pa Idris spent a few days in bed, and then died. The courthouse went with him.

Yanoh found a new boyfriend, although I had never seen the child or children's father. Yanoh and her new man began dressing in uniform, the man wearing the same shirt fabric as Yanoh's blouse, wrapper, and head tie. They drew jealous glances from the women of Leah Street, especially the *padi-padi* club of women to which she belonged. Most of them lived in a three-story wooden house next to the Idris hut. Miss Nanette, a puffy-faced mother of two boys, and her elderly father occupied the upper floor, and they rented the second floor to another single woman with one child, and an elderly couple with several grandchildren occupied the basement.

Miss Nanette, Yanoh, the woman on the second floor, and Sissy Baby formed the neighborhood *padi-padi* friendship club. They sold things in front of their houses—fruits, vegetables, firewood—and often conferenced in each other's backyard to eat and discuss new clothing styles, condemn their children's fathers in four-letter words, and tout their new boyfriends. Sometimes they stole each other's man, launched four-letter brawls over it, and went into malice mode for a few months, before coming back together and starting the cycle all over again.

"At last, she found a father for her sons!" said the *padi-padi* club. "How lucky Yanoh is. A man with style."

They stopped whatever it was they were doing when Yanoh and her man passed by.

"We're going to watch a movie," Yanoh would tell them." Or, "We're going to visit a friend in the hospital."

Then Yanoh got pregnant, and everyone in the neighborhood had a wish for her.

Attatie's cousin, who was helping to cook for us, said, "I hope this one marries her."

There was a middle-aged couple living in another tin house next to us. The neighbors called them *Aunty* and *Uncle* because of their avuncular nature, especially after a visit with Granny Kadi. Uncle said Yanoh should make sure this new father marries her, and Aunty said Yanoh should make sure he helped with the two older children.

Rumor had it that Rugie's *padi-padi* club was planning for a wedding.

But early one Sunday morning, a fight broke out.

In their church clothes, Aunty and Uncle were the first to rush into the Idris compound. Aunty wore a short, plain dress that lopsided over her high behind. And Uncle, a shirt that used to be white, a skinny tie, and a cloth rope holding his baggy black pants.

"Don't talk about her like that." Uncle put a hand over the boyfriend's mouth. "She's going to be the mother of your child."

That just ruffled the boyfriend further.

"I never want a child with a woman like her." He pulled on Uncle's tie, then gave him a shove.

Aunty succeeded in dragging Rugie closer to her tin house.

"Keep quiet," she said. "Don't use words like that on a Sunday."

"Let him stand in front of me again." Yanoh bawled. "I'll shove my foot up his ass."

"He is a man," Aunty said. "A man can use such words, but a woman cannot."

"I'll show him where his mother got him out from," Rugie continued, trying to wrestle herself out of Aunty's hands.

Everyone's attention turned to the Idris's gate from where the family matriarch had surged, carrying smoking firewood like she was leading an Olympic team, except she had only a wrapper over her breasts. Speaking in breakneck Temne, she rushed toward her daughter, wagging the firewood in the air. Yanoh saw her mother coming and tried harder to remove herself from Aunty's grip. Poor Aunty could not decide whether to let go of Yanoh and risk her running back to kick her boyfriend's ass, or to run with her, away from Mother Idris' firewood. Luckily for her, Uncle noticed his wife's dilemma and released his grip on the boyfriend, who was now surrounded by the women of Yanoh's *padi-padi* club, trying to convince him to go home.

Uncle went straight for the firewood.

"*Nntie gbot deka ka* backside!" The matriarch shoved the firewood in front of Uncle's torso as she attempted to show how she intended to use it on her daughter.

Still, Uncle entered into a struggle with her for control of the weapon. The matriarch bit her lower lips and pushed Uncle towards the gutter's edge. Uncle held firm.

The Idris boys rushed out of their yard and joined Uncle in the struggle to wrestle the firewood from their mother's hand. Helas, the angry boxer, could not display any amount of grit in front of his mother, and the younger son looked like he was about to cry.

Mammy Yanoh was proving herself a gladiator in the ring with what seemed now like the entire neighborhood's male population. Her muscles jiggled like beef on a butcher's rack as she swung them like dervishes, to the right and to the left, as their hands papered hers over the firewood. Uncle's browned-out white church shirt was now covered with ash and charcoal. Aunty stood, transfixed.

***

Papa went to the veranda and touted Mammy Yanoh's strength. Attatie busied herself preparing for her guests and shouting at us to leave the window.

Then Yanoh returned, calm and collected, and called out, "Let my mother come and shove her firewood in my backside, if that will satisfy her."

It took the men a while to cede the battle to Mammy Yanoh. It was only then that I noticed her wrapper was beginning to droop, but she caught it in time and approached her daughter, coming from one end of the street, and the daughter from the other. The men followed behind her like chicks, some posing to help keep her wrapper place.

The women reached the front of their gate and stopped. Mother and daughter observed each other, like boxers preparing for a new round. Then the mother shoved the wood in her daughter's direction, but without touching her. She spoke fast in Temne, and in her usual top-of-voice manner. I did not understand what she said, but her daughter replied that she would have nothing more to do with the boyfriend.

The Trade Board

E very woman was clutching an oversized handbag against her belly. They fanned vigorously. Some, with old newspapers. Some, manila envelopes. Others, with their head ties. They made handkerchiefs out of the ends of their wrappers. They shared chairs, two to one, large hips over the seats like hanging plants. Some sat on others' laps. Some, on the receptionist's desk. Others, on the bare cement landing. Their bodies papered the walls and darkened the corridors of Rice Board. They were waiting to buy papers, like the ones Grandpa Fabilo used to give Attatie when she first started the business.

"Hold on to my hand." Attatie prepared me for the assault across the corridor.

We stopped in front of two redwood doors divided by a thin wall. One was marked *Director*. The other, *Operations Manager*. We headed for the director's door.

"Where d'you think you're going?" the voices sneered.

A high-chested woman stood up from the receptionist's desk and put her body between Attatie and the director's door.

"Mr. English is expecting me," Attatie said.

"He's busy," the woman barked. "I've been waiting for almost an hour to see him."

The other women echoed her.

"Yes, we're all waiting to see him. We've been here since *asuba*. I woke up early this morning, washed my face, and headed straight for this office. Why should you cut in front of us."

An insurrection was about to start.

Luckily, the director's door cracked open, and a cone-shaped light seeped into the corridor. A woman in an A-line skirt and high heels emerged, clutching manila envelopes against her chest.

"Good morning, Miss Johnson," Attatie then jerked her chin forward to say, *Can I come in?*

Miss Johnson was pensive for a moment. Then she turned her head back inside the office, her hand still on the doorknob.

"Mrs. Sillah is here," she announced.

Meanwhile, I was making furtive glances behind us, afraid the women would pounce, when, like a child pulling a reluctant pet, Attatie lugged me into the office with her.

As soon as we entered the office, I understood why some men wore suit and tie to work, while others like Papa wore khaki shorts and short-sleeved shirts. Papa's office was mostly on dirt roads under the baking sun, over bridges, and in mosquito-infested bushes, while this man appeared to sit all day, behind a mahogany desk, in the freezer compartment of our fridge. I still wondered if his tailored black suit was enough protection against the freezer.

Even seated, Mr. English was a tall man with high cheekbones on a smooth skin. He was engrossed in a telephone conversation when we entered, about the arrival date of a yacht. It was not the first time I heard the word *yacht*, but the word came out of his mouth like a delicate flower. His English was dainty—the clearest I had ever heard from someone who was not an expatriate teacher.

While we waited for Mr. English to get off the phone, Attatie struck up a conversation with two men sitting in the chair in front of his desk. They inquired about the health of her family members, compared prices of rice in different parts of the city, and joked about their experiences with customers.

"You're Mameh," Mr. English said, my name sliding off his crisp voice.

As he adjusted his glasses using his thumb and index finger, I noticed Attatie's keen eye on him. *Another model for Mohammed.*

"Good morning, Mister English." I gave him a shy smile and took his delicate hand over the desk.

He joked about me carrying all of Papa's features and none of Attatie's. One of the men took Attatie's side and said I looked more like, what he called, *my sister sitting here*. Then Mr. English and the men talked business, and they left.

"We're still out here, sir. We're still waiting." The voices came as the men opened the door to leave.

Mr. English looked toward the door and said, in a crips Krio, "Unu wait, ya."

He talked business with Attatie, telling her about the next yacht, the amount of rice it contained, and Attatie's share.

As we left Mr. English's office, I continued to be amazed at my mother's ability to gain priority access in the offices of men like Mr. English. Men with overseas education and advanced degrees. How does she get them to make visits to her home, to know the names of her children, to invite her family into homes like the English's?

The crowd outside had grown. A few male traders had joined the women. Attatie took my hand for the exit. She straightened her gaze ahead of her while I stole glances at the faces of discontent shooting up around us.

"Goodbye," some of the women said sarcastically. "Maybe we'll come for help at your store if things don't work our here."

"You're welcome," Attatie replied, straightfaced.

We were already pushing down the steps when Miss Johnson cried out from behind us, "Goodbye, Missus Sillah."

Attatie went back up the stairs and ducked a few bills into Miss Johnson's cupped hand, then forayed back down the steps.

The Englishes

I wished I had not answered the doorbell. It was the English family's first visit to our house, and Attatie had not mentioned it. At least, not to us children.

"Good morning." Mrs. English perked her head and grinned, revealing a high gumline.

I pulled up the drooping shoulders of Attatie's old gown I had worn to bed, then snatched the head tie off my head. Then I remembered, my braids were half-loose. *I must look like one of these girls selling tomatoes in front of Bombay Street market.*

So now, I had to think quickly. *Do I throw the head-tie back on? But isn't it better to have a head that looked like a bird's nest on a market girl, than to present myself as a native woman with an oversized gown and head tie?*

I settled on the former and greeted the visitors.

"Good morning, Ma." I forced a smile I hoped would make up for my appearance.

"We are the Englishes." Mrs. English said.

She was first to enter as I held the door open, wearing a bold, blue dress and matching hat.

Then she introduced her children. "This is Olayinka, Theresa, Tiana, and Sylvia."

We murmured good mornings, and the four girls marched in, contemporaries of Amie, me, Fatmata, and Hassana. They wore uniform pink dresses with white frills, and pink ribboned hats.

"This is Omojowo and Olamide," she continued.

The boys were tall like their father, with parted hair reminiscent of Trinity School's Parson Samuel. The eldest of the children, they looked severe in their dark suits and navy ties, like they would rather have stayed in church.

Mr. English entered and needed no introduction. He remembered my name, and we exchanged smiles.

Now, the entire family was inside our house, standing on the narrow close leading to the parlor. For a few moments, I lost my bearing. With all eight of them in the narrow area, the space was mighty congested.

I stared from one person to the other, not knowing their reason for being in my living room. I didn't remember to offer them a seat nor take their hats.

I must have looked funny, for one of the boys cracked a smile, and the girls began to giggle.

"We're here to visit your parents." Mrs. English nudged me.

"Oh, they're upstairs," I said, and turned to run, the sound of increasing chuckles behind me.

    ***

Attatie jumped out of bed and began folding a wrapper over her nightie. Papa pulled the covers over his head and grumbled something about unwanted Sunday morning visits.

"Tell them your father and I will be down in a minute," Attatie said.

I stopped by my bedroom to change into a turquoise sleeveless dress with two pockets on its gathered skirt. It was not the kind of dress you wore for Sunday morning housecleaning, but I had to redo my image, and I hoped Attatie would not notice.

Before I could decide what to do with my hair, Attatie's slippers were already clanking down the ceramic steps.

"Who left this broom here?"

I hurried to finish undoing my braids, rushed downstairs to pick up the broom and continue sweeping the floor, making sure I stayed away from the parlor where the English children were greeting Attatie.

"Good morning, Aunty Amie." They were crisp, like their dad.

Attatie cajoled them. "My, my, what beautiful dresses!"

They giggled.

"Big men! Spiting images of you, John."

The boys looked toward their father, simpered, then bowed their heads.

"John and Veronica!" She hailed the parents' names as if they were trophies.

"A-mie!" Mr. English hailed back. "Where's Mami?"

Before Attatie could answer, Mrs. English said, "Maybe the poor man is resting. A surveyor's job is not easy, all day out in the hot sun."

"He's already up," Attatie replied. "He'll be down soon."

"You're coming from church?" Attatie said to the parents.

"Yes," the girls replied, sounding like a church choir.

"We came in for early communion," one of the boys said, as if he was in conversation with someone his age.

Surely Attatie would put a stop to this rude behavior. Children do not speak unsolicited in the presence of adults. In fact, she would soon ask all of them children to leave the parlor and go sit in the dining area.

"I like living in Wilberforce better than living in the East End," one of the girls said, now jumping to the subject of their recent move to a new house.

"We don't mind the distance," another said. "We still get to school on time."

"I see," was all my mother could say, trying to sound like an English professor listening to a student defend his thesis argument.

Then, as if looking for something to say, to defend her own lack of grit, she shouted at me.

"Mameh, did you sweep inside of this parlor?"

Well, your good visitors interrupted that, didn't they? "Yes," I replied.

I was boiling inside. I made quick broad strokes with the broom so that I could be out of their hearing. What kind of upbringing did they have? How could a family so successful, a church-going family, *good* people, raise their children to be so loose in the presence of adults? Did no one spit kola nut juice in their mouths?

I thought the parents would be soaking in shame, regretting the poor job they were doing as parents. But Papa came downstairs right at that moment, and Mr. English sounded swell.

"Ma-mie!" he hailed Papa.

Papa had changed into a white shirt and khaki shorts. He joked with the girls, pulled on what he called their *funny hats.*

Then he stood in front of the boys and said with pride, "These are the young Prince Waleans!"

With Papa now seated next to Attatie and playing host to the Englishes, Attatie turned her attention to us.

"You!" she shouted to me, over the bookcase. "Bring some soft drinks and drinking glasses."

"Mohammed!" she shouted two or three times, loud enough for him to hear from the backyard.

Mohammed finally appeared in the hallway, his hands covered in soap suds, reluctance on his face.

"What are you doing now?" she growled.

Mohammed held up his sudsy hands.

"When you're finished downstairs, the upstairs bathroom needs to be scrubbed."

"I scrubbed it last week," he groaned.

"Then scrub it again! We're not country people. We keep our bathrooms clean."

Mohammed whirled around and left, grumbling under his breath. The children giggled.

"Abassy!" Attatie screamed, two or three times.

"We don't have enough soft drinks!" I shouted, in front of the open fridge.

"Can't you come over here and talk to me?" Attatie said. "Are we living up-country?"

The girls giggled.

I moved closer to the bookcase. "Shall I get some from upstairs?"

"Bring me my handbag and call Abassy."

I reached downstairs with Attatie's handbag at the same time as Abassy was arriving in the parlor.

"Why are you standing in front of me looking like a sheep in front of a bowl of salt?" she said, when Abassy arrived.

I reminded my mother that she wanted him to go buy some soft drinks for the visitors. She looked him up and down, her pupils whirling.

"And where are you going to put the drinks? Do you think we come from up-country like you?"

"Get a towel," I told Abassy.

Abassy went off to get the towel, and I asked the Englishes, "What would you like to drink?"

The children replied, "Coca-Cola, Vimto, Fanta."

The parents asked for ginger ale and Seven-Up.

I told Abassy, "Get a pint each for the parents, and three pints for the children."

That was how children were offered soft drinks in most homes. You decide with your paired brother or sister, who gets the pint and who drinks his or her portion from a cup. You do not drink a whole pint of soft drink until you're old enough to start earning your own money.

Attatie unfolded a bundle of notes from her handbag.

"Get a pint for each person."

She zipped up her handbag and squeezed it into the space between her thigh and the chair arm.

The Griot Calls

Fatmata was a blind Djeliba, dark and erect, with butter-colored pupils and a majestic voice. She was led around town by her elementary-school-age son, in torn and dirty clothes. He would walk as straight as he could on narrow footpaths, holding one end of a long horizontal stick, and his mother the other end. Sometimes he pushed around a wooden toy car with a rope, in his free hand. While his mother sang, he lost himself playing with the car. He often looked like he had been forced out of whatever bed was, to be his mother's eyes around the few homes in Freetown that still remembered the griot tradition.

Fatmata Djeliba used to call on us on Sunday mornings. She often wore the blue fenteh cloth of the Mandinga people, though she looked like a beggar in it, with the lighter shades of blue aged into dirty black. The henna on her lips made them more plump, matching her blown-out jawbones. Her flattened flip-flops revealed fungal toenails and coarse soles.

She came one Sunday morning. Attatie was sitting in a dining room chair, facing the backyard so she could see and supervise our goings and comings. Her handbag sat next to her on the dining table. Mohammed was ironing our school uniforms. Abassy was cleaning the bathrooms. Amie was sweeping and dusting the upstairs parlor and bedrooms. Fatmata was dusting the living-room furniture. The houseboy was splitting wood, and I was sweeping the downstairs living room.

"Sillah *keh*, Jawara *keh*, Conteh, Fofanah," Fatmata sang, her silky, majestic voice obliterated by the foul smell coming off her fenteh gown.

She was standing on the backyard steps, under the window of the bedroom where Papa slept. Her son had stopped there, obviously knowing he would not be allowed to enter the house.

I was now sweeping closer to the backyard steps. I stopped to listen to her. She was singing in Mandinga, and I realized I could not understand anything she was saying. Not even Granny ever spoke to me in Mandinga. She belonged to one of those Freetown families that had witnessed the return of Africans once enslaved overseas, and as a child, had succumbed to the broken English they brought with them. She raised Papa in the Krio tongue, and both spoke only Krio to us.

Attatie grumbled, "Your granny has sent her here again to disturb us on a Sunday morning."

Djeliba Fatmata raised her voice, as if to overpower Attatie's objection, wake up Papa, and with him, the ancient glories of the Mande people.

"We don't have time for that, Fatmata!" Attatie shouted. "Today is Sunday. People are still sleeping. We're not in the country." She grabbed her handbag from the table and called out to me, "Here. Give this to her."

I stood in front of the ancient figure, and for the first time, was startled by the wild darting of her eyelids, the thick blob of her buttered pupils. She looked like she had eaten something and forgotten to wipe her mouth. Most of all, I was repulsed by the stench coming from the fenteh cloth that I had worn with pride on Prayday—the cloth that *we* Mandingas wore with pride.

Fatmata rubbed the coins inside of her palms as if to keep them warm, and launched into an avalanche of *al barakas,* promising, amongst other good deeds, that Allah will replenish the source from which they came.

"Ameena, Ameena. Go now," Attatie told her. "Today is Sunday. We need to rest."

The little boy stopped his play, took the coins from his mother, and put it inside the pocket of his dirty trousers. Then he turned around and pulled his mother and his car after him.

More Than Miss Fenella

ethodist Girls High School had a tracking system. After your second year, the school decided if you will become a doctor or lawyer, or that wise and faithful girl-Friday to a top executive or a senior civil servant. Such tracking mattered a great deal in a place like Sierra Leone, where if you are a man, you could be an inveterate drunk or a gonorrhea-infested womanizer, as long as you had a good education and were in the right profession, many parents would gladly hand over their daughters to you in marriage. Some, even in concubinage.

Young people memorized the vehicle license plates of famous doctors and lawyers, top civil servants, and politicians.

When it came to the women, especially in the legal profession, too many were unable to surmount society's tracking of them as women first. Some derided each other over men, and most subjected themselves to domestic roles not much different from the *padi-padi* club of the illiterate women on Leah Street. But even they did not fall. A few excessively indiscreet ones may see their reputations soiled, but a professional woman seldom reached dirt level.

Imagine the riot, then, when I returned from long holidays to find out I was to spend the remaining three years of secondary school in the commercial stream. According to the plan, at the end of fourth and fifth forms, I will take the Royal Society of Arts exam, not the General Certificate of Education exam that would help me secure a place in college.

Ellen Cole, Williette Frazer, Theodora Mansfield, and I sat on boulders in the school compound to consider our options. We discussed meeting with the principal, but quickly admitted that none of us wore the right knickers size to confront Mrs. Collier in a contentious setting. We all agreed that our parents were better suited to such a task. So we dug our sandals in the dirt and protested amongst ourselves, the unfairness of a system that put those girls who never did as well as us, girls with several absences, and even those whose uniform pleats were never quite straight, in the *academic stream*, solely because of what we believed was parental influence. Finally, we decided, if all else failed, on leaving the school altogether and burning the uniform.

I came home from school and dispatched Papa to Mrs. Collier's office. Attatie objected first, to what she considered an affront to a *good* principal. She believed I should be happy simply being promoted to third form—something she had not been given the opportunity to do.

"You don't understand," I bellowed. "They want me to become a secretary."

"What do you want to become, then?" she asked, throwing open her hands.

By that time, I had grown out of wanting to become a head teacher like Mrs. Jarrett, but I didn't know yet what I wanted to be. I had been exposed to trading in Attatie's store, to the occupations of men like Mr. English, and the teachers at my school, but none of them had taken hold with me the way Mrs. Jarrett did on my first day at Trinity Infant School.

"You know the secretary in my ministry?" Papa said. "Missus Cole. She's the most powerful woman in the ministry. Nobody can see the permanent secretary without going through her."

"I don't want to take shorthand and type letters," I said.

"But Missus Cole takes dictation and types letters," he replied, "and she's still the most powerful woman in the office."

"How can you be powerful if you don't write your own letters?" I retorted.

I was not yet at an age when I understood the meaning of power. What I was thinking of then was something one of my classmates had once said. Moronike gladly accepted her placement, mostly because she had an elder sister who was already a secretary. When I complained about a life of drilling shorthand in order to take good notes, Moronike simply laid back in her chair and folded her hands.

"My sister doesn't even take shorthand at the office. She just sleeps with the boss."

To me, even then, that was like being enslaved to a man my father's age. It was giving away control of my life to someone else. It was not something, even at fifteen years of age, that I was willing to settle for.

The conversation didn't get any better when Attatie, with much adulation, talked about the amount of money she and other traders gave to secretaries at the Trade Board, for access to their bosses.

"I want to be the boss you pay money to see," I said.

***

Papa made the trip to Mrs. Collier's office the next day and returned with the gloomy message that teachers had placed girls in streams they believed the girls had the best chance for success in, and all such crap.

"I moved from 1B to 2 Alpha in my first year," I stormed out of the living room. "I am clever."

Upstairs, I kicked open my bedroom door, kicked the clothes and shoes that were scattered on the floor, then collapsed on the bed and cried myself to sleep.

***

Attatie was considerate the next morning. It was a Saturday, but she didn't wake me up to go open the store. When I finally came downstairs, Amie and Mohammed had left for the store, and Papa had left for work. Fatmata and Hassana were running around in their usual play and chitchat, and Abassy was in the backyard helping Grandma Ndamba with the cooking.

I helped myself to the leftover breakfast of tea soup and bread, and poured myself a cup of tea. Attatie sat at the head of the table, watching me as though she was seeing me eat for the first time. Finally, after my last gulp of tea, she took my hand in hers.

"You've always wanted more than any of your sisters do," she murmured. "And you do better in school than all of my children." It was as if it pained her that I did well at school. "But you need to be careful." She lowered her voice even further. "You're a woman. You cannot take your sense and put it in a clear bottle for all to see."

I couldn't fathom what in the world she meant by being careful, let alone being a woman, when so many less deserving girls were going to become doctors and lawyers, while I was going to be receiving bribes for access to *big* men.

"I'm going to leave MGHS," I said. "I'm going to burn my uniform, my beret, my belt, and my school crest."

I didn't say what school I was thinking of transferring to, though I had FSSG in mind. Hassana had spent all her five years of schooling there, and she seemed to loved it.

Attatie, though, was coming up with all the *good* people that had gone to MGHS, like the wife of the manager at the Trade Board, and Miss Olive at the Ministry of Agriculture.

"I do not want to be a secretary," I told her.

"*Eheh*, she gutted, recalling someone she seemed sure would make a difference.

"Miss Fenella at Goree Street. *She* is a secretary."

"I want to be more than Miss Fenella." I got up to leave.

"Miss Fenella!" she exclaimed, watching helplessly as I left her and the table behind.

Coming to a Head in Form Four

I stood in front of form four commercial, my resentment boiling like leaves on a sweating cauldron. To begin with, the classroom was placed in one of the older brick structures behind the new building that housed the principal's office and most of the classrooms. It sat on a crooked cement pedestal, with two entrances. One opening into the dirt compound leading to the new building. The other, into a corridor that led you to the back door of the school canteen.

I selected the fourth seat on a row of desks against the wall and spent most of my first day looking outside the door.

The first teacher came in for shorthand. She introduced herself as also our form teacher. High-chested and heavy, with light skin and short hair, she folded her hands on the table and bent over it to talk, as if she was telling each person a secret.

"My name is Josephine Lamine," she said, which rattled me.

How can a Josephine be attached to a country name like Lamin?

Except for literature, I considered school a waste of time. I made friends with the most playful girls in the class, and we got into the habit of lifting our desk covers, pretending to be getting a book or pen out, while holding discreet conversations with one another.

Office duties was a class I considered especially irrelevant. It was taught by a chubby British expatriate who went around campus in short beach dresses and sandals. Miss Leckie sometimes talked in subtle Western ways that didn't reach us.

For example, when trying to teach us ethics, she said, "You shouldn't say, *My sister needs a stapler.*"

Whatever she was trying to say went over our heads, until later in the term, when she was replaced by Mrs. Lamin, who, when teaching the same chapter, said, "Do not steal office stationery."

I had the most fun in Miss Leckie's class. We had the notion in secondary school that expatriate teachers were easier than our local teachers. This was mostly because of their modern approach to child rearing which resisted the screaming and caning to which we were accustomed. We took advantage of that and felt like we had a free period each time an expatriate was teaching.

My desk was sandwiched between Memunatu Bailoh and Morondia Macauley. While Miss Leckie struggled to teach us the correct terms with which to address our bosses, and the way to welcome visitors to the office, Memuna, Morondia, and I would engage in conversations of our own. Miss Leckie started paying particular attention to us, and soon, in her frustration, would grow red with irritation, and in exasperated breath, would merge the three names as she shouted.

"Memuna! Memuna! Memuna!"

That sent the class into fits laughter. Sometimes I would start the conversations with Memuna or Morondia, just to see her turn red and get the class laughing.

***

Something happened early in the term that sent me deeper into that place I sometimes spend alone time. There was a senior girl I loved. I didn't have the courage to send her the usual letter in flowered paper and colored ink, telling her she could kiss me anytime she wanted behind the school canteen. Instead, I followed her around campus with keen eyes and ceded my place in line next to her at the fruit stall. She was glowing dark, with shiny, beaded eyes, like she could walk with them closed. She had all the qualities of a Head Girl.

To the school's criteria of strong academics, comportment and cleanliness for the Head Girl position, most of us, especially junior girls, added beauty and a well-starched uniform. We used to admire girls who were boarded at the school. Their uniforms did not have to endure packed buses and the grueling climb up the school hill. They made the easy walk from one building to another every morning and came to assembly looking prim and proper.

Mariama Deen was not a boarder, yet there was never a spot or wrinkle on her uniform. Her braids were always neatly in place. She spoke in a low, controlled voice, never laughing out loud or wandering around campus during class periods. She was already a school prefect, and always scored 95 percent and over on her report card. Her name was a regular on Mrs. Collier's fortnightly recognition at morning assembly.

I was convinced that this girl I loved was going to wear the prestigious red Head Girl button that year. Yet when Mrs. Collier announced the Head Girl position, it went not to Mariama, but to a Christian girl I thought was often too skittish around campus, with breakouts that made her face bumpy, and who appeared to never once apply starch to her uniform.

At that point, that I began spending time in those places, with people I had never met, and doubted I would ever meet. I completed the assigned novels within weeks of our beginning them in class. I read Amie's literature books and Mohammed's, and then I'd go to the bookstore and get some more. I became more conversant with characters in the books than those in real life.

Then, at the end of the school year, I read my final report sheet and swore that day would be my last. I had passed literature with flying colors, and failed every other subject. I was not promoted to form four.

From the school bus, I walked home in front of Glynis and Melissa without saying a word to them. I left the envelope with my results on top of the bookcase and went to look for the bottle of bathroom cleaner. It was almost empty. I gulped its remaining content and went upstairs, laid in bed, and waited for it to work.

The Fulani Teacher in Mini Skirt

"You don't know how much you hurt me." Papa wiped tear streaks off his bony face. "You think that's fair to me." He sounded like an aggrieved child. "I work, even on weekends, to put food on the table, pay your school fees, and make sure you wear good clothes."

He was sitting on the bed that Amie and Fatmata shared, while I sat on the one I shared with Hassana. I folded my hands on my lap and fixed my gaze on the tiles, unable to look at him.

It was him I had dreaded facing after I read my final year report. While Attatie was usually the vocal, nagging parent, quick with the stick, Papa spoke only when necessary, and seldom raised his voice at us. He was like those expatriate teachers that made us feel like we had freedom, during their classes. But now, his words hurt more than any shouting would. More than the cane on my back.

Unlike Papa's words, the cane had been sweet—a catharsis. It was the only time Papa had hit me, and it took care of the disappointment I was trying to avoid with the poison. The fainting also helped. It felt like I had died and come back.

"I will never disappoint you again." I wiped tears off my face with the back of my hand.

"I know you'll work hard and cut off the play," Papa said. "All you did this year was play."

I didn't think I had been playing. I was up against an authoritarian system that had boxed me into a controlled fate.

But I had made a promise to Papa. I meant to keep it. He was not a demanding parent. I even reconsidered Attatie's caution and decided I would take things slowly from then on. I was a woman, after all.

I will redouble attention in class and make sure Mrs. Collier calls my name at morning assembly every fortnight. At the end of the new school year, I will move on to fourth form with flying colors.

I kept my promise and started the new school year with gusto. I paid attention to subjects like history and geography, even shorthand and office duties, which I had ignored the previous year.

The chatty Mrs. Lamin was now teaching us both shorthand and office duties. Papa had gotten to meet her and found out she was married to a distant relative of his, so she considered it a duty to keep me in class during lunch breaks, with extra drilling assignments.

My name became familiar to Mrs. Collier's fortnightly list. Teachers knew my name and assigned me those little errands that only teachers' pets got—like Mrs. Lamin entrusting me with taking home her powder sponge to wash and bring back to school the next day.

***

Halfway through the term, our literature teacher was absent one day, and a light-skinned woman in a mini-skirt and Makeba hairdo came to replace her.

"Where's Missus Pratt?" someone said.

"She's sick, and I'll be teaching the class this week," the woman replied pertly. "My name is Fatu Bah. I'm from Guinea."

I'm not sure if it was the mini-skirt, the Makeba hairdo, her name, that she was from Guinea at a time that we were reading Camara Laye's *The African Child*, or a combination of all the above that did it. But the class went silent for a good five minutes while everyone stared at her, wild-eyed. I cannot say what was going on in the minds of my classmates, but for me, my mind had gone back to the beginning of my school career, after Ahmaddiyya School, when every one of my teachers had been Christian. As I matured into secondary school life, they become the women I saw in my future myself.

"I'm a student at Fourah Bay College."

The young woman's chirpy voice brought me back to the classroom.

Miss Bah was an instant hit with us. We conversed like sisters. She told us stories about growing up in Guinea, with descriptions that placed us right in the middle of *The African Child*. Unlike Mrs. Pratt, when it came to the names of people and places in the book, Miss Bah did not struggle.

Mrs. Pratt used to love reading aloud to us, but other than a few quiz questions at the end of a chapter, she engaged in little discussion of the book. She was a combination of the stern old-fashioned schoolteacher and the modern showgirl, with high heels, heavy make-up, and a no-nonsense smile. Unlike when she read a Charles Dickens or Shakespeare story, where the names would slide off her tongue as though she was native English, the Mandinga names of characters and the Guinean names of places were a challenge for Mrs. Pratt. When I heard her pronounce N'Gady—a name that one of my cousins also carried—with a long *A*, as in lane, rather than the short *A*, as in apple, I covered my mouth and chuckled.

By the end of her weeklong stay with us, Miss Bah—a Muslim girl in a miniskirt, wearing a Makeba hairdo, student at Fourah Bay College, teaching literature at Methodist Girls High School—had helped open up my world.

The Saturday Omen

If Attatie or I were not present, the rice store didn't open. That was the amount of trust my mother placed in me. She felt Amie's speech impediment rendered her incapable of much, and Mohammed could not be trusted with a good head or money. If I ever dreamed of spending my long holidays strolling with friends in the center of town, Attatie quickly pulled me back with bribery of new clothes and shoes. Or if that didn't work, with guilt, or even threats.

"What's keeping them upstairs?" she shouted, as Amie and I prepared for the trip to the store. "Do I have to come and bring them down?"

I rushed downstairs in a blue dress with pockets, its belt straps dragging on the floor behind me. We stood in front of her, waiting for instructions.

"What are you? My bodyguards?" She was pinching leaves off a jute stalk, preparing the Saturday dish.

"Hurry up and eat." She dished out our breakfast: three pieces each of sauteed sardines and boiled cassava cubes on each person's plate.

She poured milk and dumped cubes into two cups of tea and shoved them in front of us.

"How late do you think I can open the store on a Saturday and still do good business?"

"I hate sardines." I knotted a bow on my dress.

"Hurry up with that belt and sit down."

"I don't like boiled cassava," Amie cried.

"If I hear one more word from either of you," she slammed the jute leaves into a calabash, "after you threw away my hard-earned money last week, as if I pick money from the ground."

She was playing on my guilt. It had been like that since the night I sat on her bed, relentlessly spitting on my fingers to count and recount the same piles of bills. The total came up short every time. We were missing a fraction of that day's intake from the store. I was sure I had wrapped up the entire sum in one of Attatie's old wrappers and placed it in the large enamel bowl in the inner storage room. Attatie had assured me she was convinced I did the right thing, and that she suspected Mohammed, but she could not resist pricking my eyes with the loss whenever I sulked at a task.

"Where's Mohammed?" she shouted toward the downstairs bedroom where he now slept. "Is Mohammed deaf?"

"I'm not going anywhere today," Mohammed replied in a groggy tone.

"Your sisters cannot open the store without you. You know that."

"I'm tired."

"Don't make me come and drag you out of that room."

"The watchman will help them."

"We don't need him there," I said.

"You need him there," Attatie snapped. "He's the oldest, and he's a man."

Mohammed appeared in front of her, buttoning a rumpled shirt. He focused his attention on the jute leaves and frowned.

"When you own your own home, you can decide what to cook," Attatie said.

"Or he can cook his own food," I said.

"Heh-heh!" He pointed at me. "If you don't take your mouth off my business—"

"I don't want to hear any *heh-heh* talk in this house." Attatie pointed a wilted stem at him. "We're not country people."

Mohammed frowned and moved toward the door, scratching incessantly on his arm.

Attatie sent a what's-keeping-you glance at us, and Amie and I bounced up.

I felt a hand on my belt as I passed in front of her, then a weight pulling down on my pocket.

"Don't you leave without the keys." She held on to my pocket with the keys in it, until our eyes met.

Then she put her finger to her lower eyelid and pulled it down. She removed the finger and pointed it at Mohammed's back.

I nodded.

"Phone me when you arrive," she called, as I moved toward the door, her head already back over the calabash of jute leaves.

"OK," we replied in unison, none of looking back to attract more instructions.

They came anyway.

"And watch out for cars on the road. Remember, I don't want friends gathering in the store. Keep your eyes open for those price controllers."

***

Mohammed, Amie, and I were the only teenagers in the bustling crowd on Leah Street, everyone hurrying ahead of the ominous cloud of Freetown's Saturday omen. A mother carried her baby on her back, and a large basket of fruits on her head. A man driving a wheelbarrow of rubber slippers made frantic cuts in front of people.

"You think you're the only one in a hurry this Saturday morning!" someone shouted.

He ignored the complaint and continued his pursuit. A honking taxicab sped by, and a woman in a skirt, alongside a man in a shirt and tie, rushed to the gutter's edge.

On Kissy Road, in front of closed stores, a man was setting up his cigarette stall, a young girl arranging mangos on a tray. Mohammed stopped and searched his pockets next to a woman selling breakfast, then turned to Amie and me.

"What do you want? Rice *akara*, or beans *akara*?"

"Where did you get the money from?" I said.

"What do you want?" He turned to Amie.

She picked three balls of *akara*.

"You shouldn't eat in the streets." I told Amie. "Besides, we've already had breakfast."

She ignored me and accepted the bread and rice *akara*. She was never bothered by the loss of money from the store. She appeared to forget all about it the moment we left Attatie's room. But Attatie never faulted her because of her speech impediment, which she believed affected her cognitive abilities.

Mohammed gave the woman a note and turned to me in an aggressive manner.

"I'll eat in the street if I want to. I'll eat in the gutter, and I'll eat in the latrine."

I ignored him.

We reached the junction of Mountain Cut, and a girl yelled "Selassie!" from a window on the Magazine Cut side.

"Can I have a leone?" She was waving, wearing a big smile.

"Come down here and talk to me." Mohammed grinned.

The girl caught up with us in front of Trinity Church, clacking her high heels.

Mohammed threw a lewd eye on her mini-skirt. "Where're you going?"

"To hang out around town." She tugged on his shirt. "C'mon, gee me the money now. I want to take a taxi."

He wiped oil on his khaki trousers and began shuffling inside his back pocket. There were a few notes stuffed in there. He did not have a job. There were no relatives that had come around the house throwing money at us.

The girl watched him shuffle the notes in his pocket, and grinned.

Mohammed tucked a few notes in her hand. She said thanks, grinned again, then turned to face the road. His gaze pursued her skirt.

"When are we going to see?" he shouted above the din of Kissy Road.

The girl did not appear to hear him.

When we reached the Clock Tower four-road—the intersection of Kissy Road, Fourah Bay Road, Kissy Street, and Goderich Street—Mohammed tried to grab my hand, but I folded them, my anger searing.

"Attatie said I have to hold your hands to cross this road."

"I have to keep my hands on the store keys." I dipped my hands in my pockets and walked ahead of him.

We reached the cement steps where Goderich Street climbed into Lumley Street, and Mohammed took the steps, saying he was going to get Maligie Daramy's help to open the store. Maligie was a hefty, good-looking relative of ours, and the younger brother of Aunty Mbalu Baratay. His friendship with Mohammed, like mine with Hawa and Mafula, usually flourished on long holidays when we were frequent at the store.

By the time Mohammed returned with Maligie, Amie and I had felt our way into the dark room and located the heavy padlocks on the door slat. Together, we pressed on the first door until its steel curtain rumbled up enough for light to enter the store so we could locate the pushup rod. Amie pulled a chair for me to climb on. Then, while Amie shoved up my elbow so the rod could reach above my head, I latched its iron hook into a slit on the door's bar and pushed up the rod until the steel curtain screeched into its hood.

We tackled the second door, then, grinning with pride at each other, wiped our greasy hands on a piece of old cloth.

Attatie dreaded us girls opening the store on our own, especially that early on a Saturday morning, when cars were few and pedestrians trickled on Goderich Street. Children in stores had become easy targets in a city that swore by Saturday's omen—the collision you escaped on a given Saturday was destined to repeat itself the next two Saturdays. The whipping you escaped this Saturday would soak like a corn for the next two. Traders hoped for a bullish Saturday, and so did the city's army of petty thieves.

Mohammed's presence, combined with the *fangadama* mix in the cash register, was Attatie's potion against an ominous Saturday.

Amie and I were already guarding the store entrances. I sat at the door closest to the side entrance, and Amie took position at the other door closer to the cement wall that separated the store from a carpenter's shop. The sun had come out in one big splash, and we could see our rushed images on the bumpers of passing cars. Traffic was rapidly increasing on either side of the road. Pedestrians distrusted the rainy season sun, and carried their umbrellas

Mohammed and Maligie made fun of the way Amie and I policed the store.

"As if two bony girls can deter a determined Saturday robber."

"They wouldn't dare," I snapped, and hissed.

The boys giggled, dragging two chairs toward Amie's end of the store. Amie dragged her chair toward my door.

***

It was drizzling one of those slow relentless rains that challenged the mettle of a Saturday drive. There were no sales yet that morning, but it was rainy season, so I had no doubt things would pick up.

A man came hawking razor blades. He wore an oversized rappel and torn khaki shorts, with rubber slippers.

"Buy razor blade. Twenty cents," he chanted.

"I don't want razor blade," I said.

He stabbed the two boxes in Amie's direction. She looked away, and he turned back to me. It was as if he was there to protest his right to sell razor blades.

From my flat plaits right down to my sandals, there was not a feature of my appearance that didn't interest him. When he managed to take his eyes off me, it was only to begin observing Amie with equal interest. He moved a step closer, as if he was stealing his way into the store.

"Go away!" I shouted.

"Buy razor blades. Twenty cents." He shoved his merchandise in Amie's direction.

"Point the rod at him," I whispered to Amie, between giggles.

"I don't need razor blades," Amie said.

He ignored the rush move I faked toward him and began observing the piles of rice bags. He digested the image of a bag at a time, his chin moving up and down slowly, as if counting. When he finished counting, he began to string his gaze between the columns, from one side to the other, until his focus landed on the teak table with the cash register. Then he saw the telephone and the side entrance to the store.

I moved closer to Amie's ear. "This is how they study a place to raid it at night."

"Get out!" Mohammed heard me and shouted from the other side of the store.

Worms covered the man's forehead. He took timid steps backward and bumped into a woman in an embroidered print dress.

The woman gripped her handbag. "You people don't know how to walk in the city?"

His razor blades scattered on the damp cement. He revealed no emotion and said nothing. He eyed the blades with little interest as they soaked on the floor. Then, with equal languor, he stooped down and picked them up.

For a few minutes, the woman was held hostage by an onslaught of colorful wooden boxes at the back of diesel trucks, proclaiming statements like *Do Good, Believers in God Shall Never Perish, Black Man Sorry Na Laugh, No Money No Woman, Obey your Sweet Mother, Allah is Great.* They carried passengers stuffed like baggage in their latticed boxes.

The woman coughed and fanned exhaust smoke off her face, then hurried across the street at the smallest gap between two vehicles.

Mohammed got up, carrying the rod we used to open the store doors.

"Go away, you thief." He fanned the rod in the man's direction.

"Maybe he wants to buy rice," I joked.

"You don't have the money to buy this type of rice," Mohammed told the man. "This is imported rice, not the one you eat on the farm."

"Maybe we should do what Attatie always does," I bent over to talk to Amie. "We should call him into the store, take one of the blades, turn it this way and that, then say, *I'll give you five cents for all three...*"

I was waiting to hear Amie laugh, when the look on her face made my heartbeat stop. I followed her eye to see blood spluttering on the rice bags, the jamb, and the table. Then I heard Mohammed say, "I'll hit you if you don't leave my store."

The policeman who came had to push himself inside of the crowd that had already gathered in front of the store.

"Take him to the hospital," I shouted over the commotion.

I opened the bowl to give money out for a taxi, then remembered we'd had no customers that morning.

My mind ran to stories I'd heard about robbers causing commotion so they could distract and steal. Feeling helpless and afraid to call Attatie, I broke down, sobbing.

I grabbed a chair, stood on it, and with my bare hands pulled down the doors on the far end of the store. Amie began to cry, too, but she was looking around the store, more aware than I had ever seen her. She seemed to have been thinking what I was thinking.

Now, with one door closed, we both concentrated on the other entrance. I began shouting and gesticulating for the crowds to move away from the entrance. They were mostly young men from the carpenter workshop next door, and the welding shop opposite us, but they were men with whom I had never had any conversations, and I considered them mere busybodies, and maybe opportunists.

While Amie and I held the store entrance, Maligie was gesticulating an explanation to the policeman that Mohammed was not at fault, because the man had refused to leave the store. Mohammed, meanwhile, was scouting the crowd, ready to pounce at anyone who dared point a finger at him.

The building's landlady arrived from upstairs, followed by her husband in an under-vest, counting his prayer beads. She quickly arranged for the wounded man to be taken to the hospital, while her husband pulled the policeman aside to talk.

As the taxicab left with the wounded man, the boys began to cross the street back to their welding shop. Others took a right turn to the carpenter's workshop, while others, still, took a left turn towards Clock Tower.

The landlady and her husband now came into the store. The husband gave me a piece of paper with the policeman's name on it.

"Someone will have to go fetch him when your mother arrives."

"I'll go fetch him." I secured the policeman's name in my pocket.

Before they returned upstairs, the landlady shook her head and pointed at Mohammed.

"You're the oldest, Mohammed. And you're a man."

Half a Pint for Two

As the Englishes continued to breakfast at our house on Sundays after church, and Attatie became a major client at the Trade Board, the parents became our uncles and aunties. Every year, they celebrated Eid-ul-Fitr day at our house, and we spent Christmas Day with them.

We greeted the parents and went straight to the veranda to join the English children.

"What would you like to drink?" one of the girls said. "Fanta, Coke, Seven-Up, Vimto."

We each had our preference. No one wanted the same drink as the other. But Olayinka would come out with six glasses and three pints.

I should speak up. Complain. To the children, at least. That's what was going through my mind one Christmas Day.

"At our house, even on Sundays, each child got a whole pint."

I spoke up on our way home, in the back seat of Papa's second-hand Peugeot.

"Not everybody's like us," Attatie said.

Papa lifted a hand off the steering and pointed a thumb backward.

"When you run your own family, you can treat people the way they treat you."

Dancing on the Streets

With her rice business a success, Attatie became a prime candidate for godmother. Added to the means for a wedding with pomp and circumstance, she had demonstrated, in the number of years succumbed to married life, her ability to help keep a new marriage afloat.

Mammy Nenneh, the former Soso dancer, and friend of late Granny Kadi, arrived through the back door. She drank tea and ate bread and liver tea soup, entertained Attatie with some old moves from her dancing days and sang Soso songs that Attatie mouthed with her. Then she sat down to explain the purpose of her visit: That she's no stranger to Attatie's family. That she is aware that Attatie's children were in secondary school, with the attending expenses. But with all that taken into consideration, Attatie was the first person that came to mind when this great event was revealed to her.

"You're the one our entire family, and most of all, the bride, agrees will make the best godmother to her."

She justified her family's choice by recalling Attatie's performance at so and so's wedding.

"...a performance the town will not soon forget," with the crowds and the lavish food and drinks. Attatie's gold-plated chest.

Attatie thanked her for the honor bestowed upon her, acknowledged her responsibilities toward her family and the high price of things today, but said she would also acknowledge her responsibility to the larger community, and to Mammy Nenneh in particular, whom she had known since her trying days at Goree Street, when Mammy Nenneh would come and help Granny Kadi debone bonga fish. She could not, now that Allah has blessed her and her husband, turn her back on people like Mammy Nenneh.

"Allah does not pardon such actions," she said.

Of course, she would need her husband's consent to accept such an honor—a consent she was certain her husband would give, considering his familiarity with their longstanding relationship.

Now, this last part was mostly perfunctory, for Attatie, and even Mammy Nenneh, knew full well that Papa didn't wear the kind of pants that allowed him to put his foot down against his wife's desire to show off her money and new jewelry.

So Papa's consent was perfunctorily obtained, and the shopping began. For several weeks, Attatie went to the homes of her friends to show them strips of the cloth she had selected for the wedding, as godmother.

"Make sure you get the right fabric when you go to the store," she would say of the *ashobi*. "This one, where the leaves are fawn and white, on a deep brown background."

The bride also selected her own *ashobi*, and so did the Godwitness to the wedding vows, and the mother of the bride, and members of the bridegroom's family. In all, there were about five or six different *ashobis*, and some people, like late Granny Kadi's daughter, who was friends with the bride and close to Attatie, had to purchase two sets of fabrics.

The more women that wore your *ashobi*, the larger your crowd, and the more unforgettable the event. So Attatie showed strips of the fabric to even those customers at the store whom she considered *good* people or *civilized* enough to wear the same piece of cloth as she.

The entire family, including Papa, had to be involved in the planning.

"What will our Christian guests drink?"

The question was obvious to me.

"Soft drinks, of course," I replied. "And we'll have ginger beer, too." Papa chuckled. "Sugar water, the Christians call that."

"Shall was say three or four cartons of Star beer?" Attatie said.

"All right," Papa replied. "But remember, Johnson, only drinks Heineken."

"That's true," Attatie said. "And Jennifer prefers Stout."

"Oh yes, but what about Sawyer? He only takes hard drinks. What about a pint of whiskey?

"Yes. Black Label?"

The food menu was a discussion held with Mammy Nenneh, Aunty Fatmata, and Aunty Mariama, Granny Kadi's daughter, and friends like Aunty Marion.

Aunty Ijatu, the only seamstress Attatie trusted with her clothes, made our *ashobis*. She sewed my sisters and I the same style as Attatie's—a sleeveless bodice with pockets, and a gathered skirt, except that Attatie's was a top and wrapper, while ours were knee-length dresses.

When we lived on Goree Street, and I was in elementary school, I used to love *ashobi* dancing on the streets. I was about ten or eleven years old the last time I remember dancing *ashobi* on the streets, at the wedding of an older cousin, Sisi Baby Sal. It was a feeling of inclusion, even one of having grown up, wearing the same fabric as dozens of older women and copying their moves around the neighborhood to a live performance of Ebenezar Calendar's *maringa* band. We danced from Goree Street into Magazine Cut, then took a right turn into Fourah Bay Road and danced alongside taxis and other vehicles all the way to Elba Street, where we turned right on to Bombay Street and danced our way back to Goree Street.

But I was now in form four. The thought of Glynis and Melissa watching me dance in the streets with mostly women in wrappers and head ties did not appeal to me anymore. Instead, I stayed at home in my *ashobi* and helped serve the guests who, like me, had gone to school.

Mrs. Cross

My classroom in which I repeated Form four was in the lower level of a wooden building that housed our British and Canadian expatriate teachers and their families. Several wood columns rose to the spacious upstairs veranda from the downstairs level where we usually sat to discuss our collective future. Our class was almost equally divided into Muslims and Christians, but after moving in the same cohort for two years, we had coalesced into a single knot against parent and society.

From a class of a little over thirty students in my first year at MGHS, I was in a class of only fifteen girls in my fourth year. By the time we were fifteen- and sixteen-year-olds, most girls had dropped out, mostly because their parents could not continue the expenses of fees, school uniforms, and supplies, and a few others because of pregnancy. For one of the country's *good* schools, only a few were able to complete secondary school.

We had about five Christian creoles and three Christian Mende girls in the class. Then there were the Muslims made up of three creoles, one Fullah, and one Temne. We shared the values of our age and quickly grew intimate. I had become less guarded than I was at Trinity School. The kolanut juice was no longer as bitter on my tongue.

The entire class knew one girl's father was so mean, he kept an opened tin of evaporated milk in his suitcase so his children wouldn't partake of it. We knew the name of another girl's father's sweetheart, where she lived and worked. She shared her mother's warning with us, to not divorce a cheating husband for fear of losing financial support. We were privy to the last will and testament of another girl's father, who left half his wealth to his girlfriend and their daughter. There was a girl who, after her mother died, was handed over to her grandmother by a father who seldom visited them, especially when it was time to pay her school fees and buy school supplies. We learned the geography of a remote village where the only Temne girl in the class came from, and we schooled each other on the traditions and customs of our different tribes and religions.

Two of the sexually active girls filled the rest of us with lust when they talked about their exploits with adult men.

I showed the class the leather cord Attatie put around my waist. When I told them what she had said at the time, that "I'll die if a man touches it," they quickly came up with solutions like removing it myself so the man doesn't have to touch it. Something that, with my unopened eyes, I had not thought about.

The love we shared with one another in form four allowed me to spend less and less time in retreat. We expressed compassion toward every girl's situation. There was little or no distinction between those girls who lived in two- or three-story houses with electricity, and those who lived with their parents and siblings in two-room shacks and did homework under kerosene lamps. We exchanged advice on how to keep our uniforms clean, our pleats starched, our socks white, and our braids neat. If someone's hair was untidy, another person would braid it during lunch break.

I got to know Mende girls who, contrary to what I heard during my elementary school days of political meetings at our house, did not have parents with top civil service jobs, were not tribalists, and did not support any particular political party.

We shared our love letters. When you received a love letter from your boyfriend, you read it aloud in class, as if you were reading from an assigned novel. Jeers and applauses determined the boyfriend's fate. Sometimes the letter was passed around the class for each person to read. It was common for you to take home another girl's love letter to read and digest.

Annette Smith, a short, light-skinned girl with thick lenses, was reading a letter from her boyfriend.

"In the garden of love where two roses meet and shall never die…"

We *aaayed*, and *watin daated*, and *borbored*.

"Roses are red, violets are blue. My love for you will never die."

"Aaaye! Watin dat! Borbor!' *He's really in love with you. You're getting married soon!*

Mrs. Cross drifted into the classroom like a ghost. Her low-heeled flats hardly said a word on the cement floor. It felt like a cold storm had enveloped the room. She was never generous with her smiles. The only emotion she appeared to know how to express was loathing, for non-Christians, and those Christian girls who did not understand the importance of religious knowledge, which in our school, was a euphemism for Bible studies.

It was customary for teachers to give little speeches before retuning tests.

"I was disappointed with your work," they would say. "I don't know if I have to split open your heads and put the book inside."

Blah, blah, blah, and blah.

They also had the habit of returning tests in scoring order so that the student with the highest score got her paper first, and the longer you waited for your paper, the worst you did, so that the last person got up to receive her paper amidst suppressed giggles.

Mrs. Cross sat down and held our test papers hostage under her palms as she began her address.

"I do not know," she barked, "why you Christian girls allow Muslim girls to beat you in religious knowledge."

I sat in the front row with bowed head, praying I wasn't amongst the Muslim girls that had crossed the path of the beast. I prayed it was a girl like Isatu Bah, who was usually able to talk back to teachers.

Mrs. Cross finally let go of the first paper and spit out my name like a dog vomits spoiled food. I was the Muslim girl that Christian girls allow to beat them in a test about the Bible.

Sweat flooded my armpits. I gathered my fingers and twisted them, as if breaking them would remake me into a child whose parents could not buy kerosene for the lamp that would have allowed me to study for the test.

Luckily, only a tiny space separated my desk from the teacher's. I had to stand up only as a sign of respect and didn't need to make the walk to her desk. Still, my legs wobbled under the strain of her owl-like eyes as she shoved the paper into my hand. I managed a meek thank you.

The class ended without me taking in anything she taught that day. I made a conscious effort to not understand her lecture, to not offend her by knowing the answer to questions that Christian girls could not answer.

Mrs. Cross left. Annette resumed reading her love letter.

"Aaaye! Watin dat! Borbor!"

I could not rejoin in the fun. I was wondering if I was right in offending a teacher. I knew teachers had the right to stifle my opinions simply because they were older. But did they have the right to stifle my progress?

I knew exactly how my mother would react to word of me offending a member of that group she called *good* people. I also remembered how she reacted when Miss Jackson asked for too much money for the parsonage.

Ramadan

The *civilized* schedule we followed at home—of breakfast before school, and dinner and homework before bed—was mostly thrown out like dirty dishwater during the month of Ramadan. I had stopped going to Islamic lessons since we moved from Goree Street, and other than the obscure *karamoko* that Attatie brought home every now and then to teach us the Qur'an after school, and the *maghrib* prayers we held as a family, I was mostly a Wesleyan girl, gladly participating in the obligatory morning prayers and Bible studies, and striving to live a life of hard work, integrity, and friendship with my peers.

Just like Papa had left the choice of secondary schools to us, he did the same with Ramadan prayers. With the setting of the sun, Papa donned his fez and rappel to pray amongst his uncles and cousins in the Mandinga community at Magazine Cut. Mohammed grabbed a prayer rug and rushed to any of the fastest and most current *express* prayer locations, mostly on street shoulders and pavements, to complete the hour-long prayer in less than fifteen minutes. Depending on her capacity to stomach mother-in-law, Attatie alternated between Soso Mosque and sitting on the veranda to pray with Pa Idris. My sisters and I threw on our headscarves, held hands, and joined the hurried crowds descending towares the Soso Mosque.

Just as you could attend Ahmadiyya School from Granny's yard, you could pray at the Soso Mosque from her yard. Together with our cousins from Goree Street, Jenkins Street, and Cardew Street, and those living at Granny's house, we spread reed mats on granny's yard, or the untarred street, and throughout prayers, we gossiped and giggled at the shadows of hurried latecomers.

Usually, Attatie had to send Mohammed to get us, because even after prayer was over and the adults had left, we stayed on our mats, enjoying the moonlight. Or we went inside and ate leftovers from Granny's Ramadan dishes.

It was hard doing homework after returning home. Fatmata and Hassana went to bed, but Papa insisted Amie and I do homework. He sat at the table with us and helped us put our bookbags on the table or picked up a pencil that had fallen on the floor, or assisted with a difficult math problem.

Attatie went to bed, saying she had to get up before the rest of us in the early morning hours to prepare *sogoli*.

"Christian girls do not have to go to *nafila* and stay up to do homework," I groused, as she was leaving.

"You're not Christian girls," she shot back.

Paying Back the Uncles

Papa always began his obligatory Ramadan charity on the first week of fasting. He bought provisions like tin milk, cocoa, Ovaltine, and sardines, together with a bag each of rice and sugar, which he measured into dozen cups and distributed, along with the provisions at the goldsmith workshop.

Maybe because they were his priority for *sunakati*, Attatie would repeat her mantra, mostly to us children, that Papa paid more attention to his uncles and their families than he did us. His uncles were only about ten to twelve years older than him. When Papa wasn't on the veranda after work, drawing land plans, he was at their goldsmith workshop listening to the extended family problems that were adjudicated there.

Four of Granny's five brothers owned the shop where they hammered gold bars all day, on sooty anvils. Attatie said all they did in there was put their mouths in other people's business.

Maybe she had a point. I never once saw a showcase in their workshop, and I don't remember ever seeing customers in there. I doubt very much they sold the jewelry they made to anyone they didn't know, or anyone who didn't come recommended. What they called *customers*, were mostly relatives and friends who stopped by to chat, or to announce the birth of a child, to bring news of a death in the family, to inform them of the date for a 40th Day or a one-year ceremony, or to lodge a complaint. During such visits, Grandpa Abdul, in a long kaftan, would hold a pair of thongs over a coal pot furnace and decide that the set he was making would be a gift to the bride to be. At other times, the talkative Grandpa Osman, sitting in front of a chipped wooden table with hammers and chisels scattered in front of him, would add the final ring to a necklace and use it to appease an aggrieved party to a complaint.

Their wives, like most uneducated women in Sierra Leone, were hardworking petty traders whom Attatie thought their husbands did not deserve. They also survived through donations from the recipients of their gifts, or work orders from those friends and family members like Attatie, who insisted on giving them something for their effort.

Their workmen were mostly recalcitrant sons and nephews—a child who needed to be kept away from bad company, or one who had to be shown that life was not a bed of roses. He would be given the arduous task of working the leather bellows or washing crucibles at the shop. It was a threat Papa often used to keep Mohammed in line.

I confronted Papa with Attatie's concern that he spent more money on his uncles and their families than he did on us. We were age-groups with their children, and we called them cousins, rather than uncles and aunties.

The provisions were scattered over the dining table, and the bag of rice laid on the floor, against one of the table legs. There were about six or seven small cartons also on the floor.

"You don't know how lucky you are," he replied, his attention on the cups of rice he was counting. "Do you know what those uncles did for me?"

I could not imagine what a group of fez-toting goldsmiths in long kaftans, and with an elementary-school education, could have done for him.

So I replied, "They do not do anything for you. You do everything for them and their children."

"You see those little bowls they put on the fire to melt gold?" he said.

I nodded, thinking of the dirty crucibles that are always strewn around the workshop.

"Each year, when my school fees were due, they passed one of those bowls around."

His face grew solemn as he looked into my eyes.

"Each uncle gave what little he had so that I could go to school."

"But Granny sold *agidie*," I said. "You told us so yourself. And you used to peddle *agidie* after school."

"The *agidie* helped us a lot," he replied. "But how many people eat *agidie* instead of rice?"

I understood that. Most people ate the hardened corn porridge only when they're ill and needed food that could slide easily down their throats.

He explained the difficulties, even in his days, of a single mother sending her sons to school, let alone a *good* school, on three pence from each *agidie* sale. Then I heard about it for the umpteenth time, about him walking to school barefoot. Granny able to scratch to buy only his uniform and books. And how, in the end, most of the boys with whom he played football and cricket, boys like Ambassador Abrahams and Dr. Stuart, going to England after secondary school, while he settled for the local training school for surveyors.

He spread his hand over the cartons of provisions. "This is nothing, compared to what they did for my education."

I may not have agreed with him then, but I understood why Papa never contradicted his uncles.

***

It was hard to eat under the quiet of night, with my eyes still dropping in sleep. For *sogoli* meals, my sisters and I encouraged our sleepy stomachs by abandoning Attatie's liver tea soup for *foofoo* with pale sorrel soup, drank Coca-Cola instead of rice pap, and ate crackers instead of beans cake. I ate almost until dawn prayer time, and drank as much as my stomach could hold, hoping to satisfy my thirst for the day of fasting ahead.

It didn't matter how late Amie and I returned to bed after the pre-dawn meal, Papa came to our bedroom and rubbed his wet hands from ablution, on our faces. We got up and prayed, then stole supplemental sleep in a bathroom, behind a couch, or even standing up.

"I need you to help me remember the names of *good* people," Attatie said one morning, when I was leaning against the dining room wall. "I forgot to include Mister and Missus Evans on my list last year. I must give them something this year, even twice, to make up for forgetting such important people."

I was yawning and rubbing my eyes as I tried to think of names of Attatie's Christian friends and acquaintances.

"Get a book," she said. "Write on the front cover, *Sunakati Book.*" Then she straightened. "Write also, *Ramadan Charity Book.*"

Mohammed and Amie joined me, and we brainstormed names of every adult friend and family member of our parents. I filled two and a half pages with names and dates on which each family will be sent their rice pap *sunakati*. She pulled down the book in my hand and looked at the list of people I had written down, as though she could read.

"That is not enough," she said. We need to fill up the page. I added names of appropriate neighbors like Glynis's mother, Melissa's parents, Mr. and Mrs. Scale, Mr. and Mrs. Candy, and Mr. and Mrs. Walcott-Taylor, until the page was about three-quarter full. Then I started calling out the names I was adding to complete the page.

"Miss Nanette, Sisi Baby, Aunty and Uncle—"

Attatie snatched the pencil from my hand. "Sisi who? Miss who?"

"But they're our neighbors, too," I said. "And Sisi Baby had helped with Granny Kadi's funeral. She, Miss Nanette, and Aunty and Uncle are Christians.

"Have you ever seen them go to church?"

"Sisi Baby went to church on Christmas Day. And Aunty and Uncle go to church some Sundays."

"Have you ever seen dishes that look like mine in any of their homes?"

I had not. But then again, I was not a frequent visitor to their homes.

"We'll use the everyday dishes," I pleaded.

"If they are Christians and they cannot live like *good* people," Attatie said with deep scorn, "what good are they to anyone?"

In the end, we sent them rice pap in the dishes on which we served everyday food.

Another Ramadan ritual at our house was bringing out from storage Attatie's enameled steel dishes with painted flowers. They were dishes that went to the homes of *good* people, and locked back up after Ramadan, to be brought out again only for a wedding or another special occasion. Attatie used the dishes to serve rice pap, a staple during the month of Ramadan at our house, as well as in most Muslim homes in the city. Believing that only she could cook rice pap that maintains that newly harvested rice flavor, she didn't leave the cooking of her porridge to anyone, not even to Granny Kadi when she was alive.

So the preparations started with pots, pans, and wooden spoons that were used only for cooking rice pap. From the moment the rice grains were left to swell in water, no source of foreign taste or odor was allowed near it.

The houseboy pounded the soaked rice in a mortar reserved for pounding rice and sieved the flour into a calabash or a bowl, similarly reserved, and carried it on his head to the store. At the store, while touting the quality of her rice to a customer, Attatie would put the calabash of flour between her legs and sprinkle water to moisten it.

At the same time as she was directing us to make a tester available to a customer, she would be kneading the flour with her bear hands. As she was directing a laborer to lift a rice bag, she began breaking up the large rice balls that had formed and rubbing them into smaller pieces, turning them over this way and that. By the time she was watching Amie and I count the money and thanking the customers for their patronage, she was already bouncing the nipple-sized balls against the calabash and getting ready to pour them into a large tray to be placed on the houseboy's head for the trip back home where he would leave the rice balls out in the open to dry.

***

The entire house moved at a brisk pace on Sundays because *good* people stayed home and relaxed on their verandahs after church, or if they didn't go to church, rested to regain their strength for the new week ahead. It was the best time to enjoy Attatie's rice pap and the light and fluffly beans *akara* dish she added on the side.

On the first Ramadan after Papa bought his second-hand Peugeot, I was writing down names in the Sunakati book during our post-Fajr brainstorming sessions, when Attatie buttonholed Papa as he headed upstairs.

"I want to send some rice pap and beans *akara* to some of your friends at work."

Papa, who, after his Sunakati to his uncles, usually showed little interest in Attatie's own charities, called out the names of only two colleagues, both East Enders.

Attatie scratched her neck. "But Mister McQueen, the permanent secretary. What about him? He has been very supportive of you, and he came to our open house."

Papa shrugged. "McQueen lives all the way in Tengbeh Town." And then he went on about the futility of a child carrying a tray of rice pap all the way to Tengbeh Town.

Attatie pulled the strands of her braids under her head tie.

"But we have a car now."

Papa did not respond.

"I'll put the bowl in a deep basket, and Mameh will hold it on her lap in the back seat."

Attatie had a rule when it came to delivering rice pap during Ramadan. Mohammed made the faraway trips that included crossing streets with heavy traffic. Amie and I covered East End areas like Goree Street, where we had grown up. However, as Amie and I grew older, we began to insist that we, too, could make crossings with heavy traffic while carrying a trayload of hot food on our heads. Especially since Mohammed received heavier *lunch money* than we did when he went to non-relatives who lived farther away from us.

In small tests and trials, Attatie began allowing me to make the longer trips—first, to her friends at Fourah Bay, where I would grip the tray with both hands above my head and take the sidewalks of Kissy Road right down to the junction of Savage Square. Then, with gingerly steps, while slowly turning my heavy head load to the right and to the left, and the right again, I made my way across the street into Savage Square. I maneuvered the narrow inner streets of Fourah Bay in the same way, so that by the time I was sixteen, I was making the same complex trips as Mohammed.

On the Sunday afternoon when Papa was ready to leave on his first delivery trip, I sat in the car with four large bowls of rice pap, and four smaller ones with beans *akara* in them. In addition to Mr. McQueen, we made deliveries at Congo Cross and Brookfields, to a Mrs. Sawyer and a Mr. Sanusi, whom Attatie had been longing to include in her Sunakati book. Amie and I were pleased, though, because we received about ten leones each in lunch money.

That Sunday, Attatie added another category to the Sunakati book:

a Sunday delivery to people we could only reach by car.

The Idris Boy Makes Good

The Idris son looked like a real seaman, leaned against his zinc gate, holding a pint of beer and smoking a cigarette. He wore a new pair of jeans and short-sleeved shirt with its collar turned up. He had just seen off some friends who had been making merry with him, and from my window, I could see beer pints and cigarette stubs scattered around the only doorway of their tin hut.

I didn't know Papa was on the upstairs veranda watching him, until I heard him call out, "You, Bockarie! Come up here right now."

Bockarie quickly put out his cigarette and left the beer pint on the brick step.

While the girls seemed intractable, Papa had an amount of influence over the Idris boys. Bockarie's younger brother sometimes came to do his school homework in the dining room with us after his return from hawking fruits. Attatie never failed to call Mohammed's attention to him.

"Look. A boy without electricity in his house, and he still finds a way to do his homework."

Papa would point to the backs of the Idris children and remind us, for the umptieth time, of the *agidie* he peddled in his Model Elementary School uniform.

Bockarie had been gone for months, and when he returned, the angry boxer countenance had disappeared. Numerous friends came and went, took strolls with him, and brought him girls. We were told he had gone to sea, and he returned with enough <u>dough</u> to show it.

When I opened the door for him, he looked me deep in the eye and bowed before entering. Not only were his eyes peaceful, but his voice was tolerant when he said hello, which I think was the first time he ever spoke to me. Then, out of nowhere, and without saying any-thing other than the hello, he dipped his hand in his pocket and gave me a ten-leone bill. I took it from him and said thank you, and then he stood aside for me to lead him to Papa upstairs.

Bockarie spent almost an hour with Papa, then left and returned with a stuffed duffle bag that Papa later delicately carried into the bed-room with him.

Only a few days after that, half-clothed men began going in and out of the Idris compound with sticks and stones. One of them would make a visit with Papa on some evenings, and once or twice, Papa went into their yard—something Attatie thought bordered on extreme behavior.

"Your father does things that people in his station should not at-tempt." She observed him from their bedroom window.

Before we knew it, a brick structure was coming up in the Idris compound, and Papa was proudly announcing that Bockarie was build-ing his own house in his late father's compound.

England, Where You Could Pick Thinks Off the Ground

Granny told the story several times. It was Papa's friend, Chaka Abrahams, who absorbed the blow of rejection, and begged and reduced himself to comedic fits of coaxing to win over Attatie's heart for Papa. Later, when Chaka was leaving for England to study, he asked Papa to keep a watchful eye on Jennifer, his girlfriend. Either Papa didn't do a good job, or there were what Granny called *bad people determined to remove bread from Jennifer's mouth.*

The rumors started, Granny said, as soon as Chaka got off the boat. Like every young man with an overseas education, he was ready to marry his sweetheart, Jennifer.

"They lied and said she had been unfaithful during Chaka's absence. So I organized a meeting." They all came here and sat on those chairs." She pointed to the now flattened cushions. "Chaka, Jennifer, your father and mother, and some close friends."

"I made them a very nice meal of fish stew," Granny recalled. "They ate and talked and ate and talked. And in the end, Chaka decided he'd go ahead and marry his beloved Jennifer."

That was part of the history behind our Christmases at the Abrahams's. Every year, we would set out in the early afternoon, spend some time with the Englishes at Wilberforce, then drive to Lumley to spend the rest of the evening at the Abrahams. It happened every year. We were barely out of the car before Uncle Chaka and Aunty Jennifer would appear on their front lawn and begin shouting old joke lines

at Papa and Attatie; the couples would giggle and pull at each other's
arms, like teenagers.

When the play ended, Aunty Jennifer would turn to us and say,
"Don't just stand there like strangers. Go help yourselves to some food
and drinks."

At the Abrahams's we helped ourselves, each to a pint of soda.

***

Uncle Chaka was permanent secretary at one of the government
ministries when he was appointed ambassador to Britain. I think it was
to celebrate his first Independence Day in Britain, that he asked Papa
to send him a gown. I guess Uncle Chaka was not going to represent
Sierra Leone on British soil, on Independence Day, in the suit and tie
of his colonial heritage.

Of course, it was Attatie who went in and out of their bedroom to
bring out Papa's best gowns hanging on either hand. She put them on a
chair, picked up the gold one, held it out against her body and asked for
Papa to look at it, as though Papa had never seen his own gown before.
She explained Uncle Chaka's skin color to Papa—more copper than
the fawn of Papa's skin. She made him select the best color for Uncle
Chaka's skin. Then she refused his selection as that of a man who
knows nothing about fashion, and went for a fenteh gown instead, and
a dark blue fez she felt matched the fenteh and Uncle Chaka's skin.

After Uncle Chaka received the gown, he wrote back, "Let us
know what you and the children would like from England."

No one ever made such an open offer to Attatie of things from
England. It was what she liked most about Uncle Chaka, she said. He
was indulgent.

Papa sighed and said Uncle Chaka didn't know what he had gotten
himself into.

Attatie called all six of us into the living room and asked each
person to make a list of all the things he or she wanted from England.
Mohammed wanted a football, shirts, trousers, and shoes. Amie and
I wrote down dresses, shoes, umbrellas, handbags, half-slips, school
socks, and raincoats. Fatmata and Hassana wanted dolls and any other
toys, dresses, shoes, underwear, umbrellas, raincoats. And Attatie wanted twelve-yards of lace, two pairs of shoes, slippers, a dozen half-slips,
three or four handbags, raincoats, umbrellas, a nightie, and a brassiere.

For Papa, who refused to add to an already incumbered list, she added shoes, a raincoat, and a suit.

Attatie had me combine everyone's list into one, and every day, while we waited for Papa to take the list to the ministry of foreign affairs to be delivered by diplomatic pouch, Attatie thought of a new item: a Lady Marlene brassiere—instead of the short ones, a particular style shoe she had just seen on someone's feet.

When we heard the Abrahams were coming home on leave, Attatie prepared us for the gifts they were bringing. So when when Aunty Jennifer sat down and placed a small plastic bag marked Marks & Spencer on her lap, I strained to peer around her. Attatie called for me to bring my aunty a drink and a glass.

Aunty Jennifer poured the ginger ale into the glass and then opened her purse and took out a crumbled paper I recognized to be the list we had sent by diplomatic pouch. Then she lit a cigarette, and Attatie asked me to bring an ashtray. Now, she went back into her purse and brought out a pen, then crossed her leg.

"I went through the list you sent," she said, "but most of these items were difficult to get in England."

"Mmmm," Attatie said, looking deviously into her eyes.

"To begin with," Aunty Jennifer slanted her head, "the raincoats they have in England are too thick for the weather in Freetown, and the umbrellas are too thin for our heavy rains."

Attatie said, "Mmmm."

Then Jennifer went on to explain the way the rain in England comes down, vertically, as opposed to the slanted strokes of the Freetown rain. The socks children wore in England were thick because of the weather, and not the thin ones we wore to school in Freetown. It was the same for the school sandals, which she said were different from the covered sandals children wore to school in England.

So one, by one, she ticked off an item after explaining why it could not be found in England.

Poor Attatie! She had never been to England, so she could not make any opposing points.

Her case successfully made, Aunty Jennifer opened the Marks & Spencer bag and brought out a white nylon half-slip and a brassiere in

Attatie's size. They were the only items, she said, that one can safely purchase in England for use in Sierra Leone.

"What a liar!" Attatie said, throwing the plastic bag on a chair. "How much different it would have been had Chaka not been too lazy to do the shopping himself. And she had the chest to sit there," she pointed to the empty chair, "cross her skinny legs, puff cigarette, and say things were not available in England. England, where you can pick things off the ground."

She picked up the Marks & Spencer bag again, opened it, and put the brassiere across her chest.

"This is not even my size."

Then she put it down and took out the half-slip, stretched out the elastic and said that also was not her size.

She returned the items in the plastic bag.

"How skinnier she had gotten. The only person to spend an entire year in England and not gain even a few pounds."

I offered to wear the half-slip if it didn't fit her, but she didn't appear to hear me.

"Look at all the things Mrs. English brought from England the other day. Not to mention, Missus Sawyer and Missus Johnson."

When Push Comes to Shove

I was already dressed for school when I answered the doorbell for a woman in an old, embroidered print dress with a scarf tied around her head. Her face was drawn, her eyes not quite open. Until she called my name and asked how I was doing, I did not recognize her.

Before I could ask her in, I heard the clacking of Attatie's slippers on the ceramic staircase. She came down squeezing her handbag under her arm as she curled her body sideways to tie her headscarf.

"Have some breakfast," Attatie told Aunty Marion.

"Don't worry, Amie. I'll be all right," she murmured.

"How about something warm for the stomach. Just a cup of tea."

"No, Amie. Don't worry. Let's get going."

Attatie did not eat breakfast either. She took her friend's hand, and together, they disappeared into the early morning dawn.

Aunty Marion visited a few days later. Attatie took her upstairs. On the living room settee, they whispered together a few minutes, then Attatie handed her a small parcel which she quickly ducked in her handbag. I knew immediately what their predawn visit had been about. Attatie was repairing the cord between her Christian friend and the world of the ancestors.

***

The first time the Englishes came without the eldest son, I was the first to ask about him.

"Olamide didn't come to church today," one of the sisters replied.

Attatie came downstairs and asked the same question, and the mother answered this time. Then Papa came down, and the father replied that Olamide makes his own decisions nowadays.

On another Sunday, I noticed that as soon as breakfast was over and the Englishes began moving into the living room, Attatie and Mrs. English moved upstairs to whisper things between them on the settee. Attatie did most of the talking, cupping her mouth and rubbing her face with one hand, then moving the same hand up and down one arm as if to show Mrs. English how to take a bath. Mrs. English nodded gravely. Then Attatie placed an object in Mrs. English's hand, and the latter made a move reminiscent of Aunty Marion, as she secured the object in her handbag.

I heard from Mohammed later that Olamide had stopped going to school because he was on drugs. The details were scare. He was still at home but lived more like an non-paying tenant than a member of the family.

Then after dusk one day, an old man in kaftan came and set up a sweating cauldron in our backyard. Not long after, the Englishes car stopped in front of our house, and Olamide toddled behind his mother towards the backyard, where the man in the kaftan was waiting.

***

Not long after that, on a Saturday morning after Papa had left for work, the old man in the kaftan returned. Attatie set him up in Granny Kadi's old room downstairs. This time, it was Aunty Marion who came, covering her head in a silk bandana.

"Have patience, my sister. Things will turn around soon," Attatie was telling her, as they entered the room.

Maybe Attatie had called me to pick up the dirty clothes we had left in there, or I used that as an excuse to eavesdrop. Pa was sitting on a reed mat, his back leaned against the siderail. Pebbles were scattered on the mat between him and Aunty Marion. Attatie sat on the bed's edge.

"She's not sleeping at night," Attatie was saying.

Pa's eyes were glued to the stones. "This woman who has stolen your husband's attention—do you want her to die?"

"Well…" Attatie looked around and saw me stooping as I pretended to be picking things off the floor.

On the one hand, she wanted to ask me to leave the room. And on the other, she wanted to address this enormous question that Pa had just put down. So since Aunty Marion seemed shocked herself by the question, Attatie decided to ignore me, brought her thumb and index fingers to her nose, and let out several nervous sniffs.

"That would solve my sister's problems," she said. Then murmured, "If only she didn't have children."

Pa asked Aunty Marion, "Are they your husband's children?"

She said they were not, but that she wouldn't want any child to be without a mother.

"We just want him to leave her," Attatie said. "He should stop going to her."

She repeated the move, several times, crossed her arms over her breasts, and released them.

"Leave her completely," she said with force. "Whenever he goes to her house, he should feel as if he is in a latrine. He should smell shit all around him until he leaves. He should never want to go there again."

Aunty Marion's nods were gaining severity.

"I will give you something to rub on your skin," Pa said, "so that when he is close to you, he will not want to leave the house. He will stay with you all the time."

"Don't make it too strong," Attatie said. "She has to go to church."

But Aunty Marion said she would wear anything to get her husband back.

"No, no" Attatie said. "Don't bring yourself down to the level of a country-woman."

Attatie's caution cut deep into the wound that Aunty Marion was nursing.

"Look at me, Amie." She funneled her fingers and pulled out her print dress. "Can anyone go as low as I have come? My husband is a senior civil servant. Look at the old rags I'm wearing."

"Indeed." Attatie bowed her head.

"How many times a month do I see him? What is wrong with my house? What is wrong with me?"

"Nothing, my dear. Nothing at all."

Aunty Marion's voice was beginning to crack.

"A man for whom I carried beer bottles on my back."

"Indeed, that's the curse of today," Attatie murmured. "The baboon works, and the monkey eats."

"Where was this woman, Amie, when I had to do hair all night so that my husband could afford a taxicab to work the next day?" The tears were streaming down her cheeks now.

Attatie still had her head down, now slanted to one side, while she fidgeted with her wrapper edge.

"Where was she, Amie? Where was she?"

The sorcerer was absorbing all of this with the air of a controlled spectator. I could tell that he was no stranger to the cries of the defenseless.

"This is not just my husband we're talking about, Amie. This is my labor. I worked hard to help that man get where he is today. Look at me, Amie. People laugh behind my back. I have to beg and borrow to go out looking decent."

Pa said, "Do you want to kill her?"

Attatie lifted her head as though coming out of a dream.

"Take those outside now," she said to me.

What Was Her Name Again?

In religious knowledge class, Mrs. Cross was telling us that only those who believe in Christ will get to heaven. With King James's Bible flat on her table, she hunched forward, folded her hands on her stomach, and proselytized.

"And the Lord Jesus sayeth, none goes into the Lord but by me."

Her gaze, with eyes like those of a dead fish, spread lazily over the class. When they rested on me, I fidgeted with the pages of my Bible.

"What does that mean?" she asked, rhetorically.

Her voice was usually like a balloon whose air had been drained out, until she talked about those things Jesus Christ said.

"The Lord Jesus Christ is saying," she preached, "that those of you who do not go to church on Sundays, you have not secured for yourselves a place in heaven."

Annette raised her burly hand. Mrs. Cross leaned back on the chair as though afraid to break its back.

"It means that all those Muslims who do not go to church will not go to heaven."

The class broke into a loud chortle that lasted only long enough for everyone to be aware of Mrs. Cross fury.

She moved on, the contortion on her face still visible, as she read from another passage where God cursed the Philistines. Her eyes dilated, as she spread her thin arms over our heads, twisting and cupping her lips to describe the floods and plagues that God could bring upon those who did not go to church. She reminded me of Alpha Ghazali's explanation of Allah's damnation of Abilaabi.

I raised my hand, and Mrs. Cross' eyes brightened. Her stiff slips parted, and she ventured a half-smile. She probably thought I was going to ask to be saved.

"Allah did the same thing to Abilaahbi," I said. "In the Qur'an, Abilaahbi betrayed his nephew, the Prophet Mohammed, and Allah cursed him so everything he touched turned bad."

The room was silent as I explained Abilaabi's plight, using all of Alpha Ghazali's imagery.

"He could not even touch his wife's gold jewelry, for it turned into brass."

By the time I ended my explication, Mrs. Cross' eyes had turned back to those of a dead fish.

"We're not the same people," she barked. "The Bible does not call for the genitals of girls to be mutilated."

I had not read the Qur'an, so I didn't know if it called for the genitals of girls to be mutilated. But even if that was the case and I was aware of it, I doubt very much I would have contested my teacher.

I brought my head down to the Bible on my desk. Then Annette gave Mrs. Cross another opening.

"And they say we are dirty because our genitals are not mutilated."

Now, Mrs. Cross put the Bible aside to talk about the books she had read when she was living in England with her husband. The class chuckled, of course, when she mentioned her husband, but she was too much into herself to notice.

"Those of us who've been to England," she said, "know everything that happens in those so-called secret societies where they mutilate girls. We read about it in books over there. What you Muslims do not know is that it is only when you accept the Bible do you become civilized."

I felt her eyes on me. I pretended to be reading my Bible, while under my breath I prayed; "I hope, as soon as you get home today, your drinks more alcohol than he ever did, lifts up your dress and puts the strokes on your bare flesh."

The Prizegiving Essay

Mrs. Cross ceased teaching us religious knowledge half-way through the term. She was replaced by Miss Benjamin who was also our class teacher and taught us English. Mrs. Benjamin gave no explanation for the change, and no one asked for one. I was just glad I was not going to continue a pawn in Mrs. Cross's abusive marriage.

Miss Benjamin was a recent graduate of Fourah Bay College. Short and ropy, with copper skin and a quick gait, she reminded me of Miss Bah. Unlike Mrs. Cross who never got up from her seat, Miss Benjamin started every class matching around the room holding a Bible in the air.

"Bibles! Bibles!" she would cry, as though she was hawking them.

Every girl had to place her Bible on the desk for her to see. There was a girl named Isatu Jalloh who was taller than Miss Benjamin. Isatu never brought a Bible to school. For two consecutive classes, Isatu endured Miss Benjamin insisting she brought a Bible to class.

Then, in the third class, when Miss Benjamin asked her, "Why do you still not have a bible?" Memuna looked her straight in the teacher's eye and said, "Because I'm not a Christian."

There were enormously few girls who could address a teacher in that way. For one thing, you did not look a teacher in the eye, let alone talk back to her. Secondly, like every other teacher, Miss Benjamin carried a cane. But on that day, it was most likely Isata's height that saved. For the rest of the semester, she entertained herself looking out of the window when Miss Benjamin told us Bible stories.

Miss Benjamin left her religion behind in literature class. She opened for us, new and challenging ways of thinking about writing.

She would have us write three-page essays describing obscure objects like a straight pin.

"How about a safety pin?" we would say.

"No," she'd reply in a jovial tone. "That one already has too many parts to it. I want you to use your imaginations. Dig deep into them."

For most of the term, we described water, a blade, a pebble. By the end of the school year, we began putting our descriptive practices into writing about ourselves.

We had to write an essay about something with which we struggled. My first thought was Mrs. Cross. It was an opportunity to reveal my hidden ire, to write down that which I could not speak out. But I was sixteen and still a child, albeit in society's eyes.

Mrs. Cross was a meanspirited woman in an abusive marriage, but she was my mother's age. On top of that, she was my teacher. There was no case between a child and an adult, let alone a teacher. Claiming she had wronged me was tantamount to admitting I had done something wrong.

It was the week after our school's yearly prize-giving service for students who had performed exceptionally well in different subjects. Prizes were also given out for general Wesleyan behavior such as helping teachers, good attendance, cleanliness, and overall good conduct. I was going to be receiving a prize for English.

Chairs were brought out into the schoolyard for a church service, and a school play after the prize giving. Of course, parents and family members were invited.

My parents never attended school functions, especially not when they included church services. Papa said he did well without Granny ever meeting his teachers, and Attatie wouldn't know how to talk to my teachers. So I donned my school uniform and the ceremonial straw hat, with black shoes and white socks, and went on my own to receive my prize. Leaving the East End of Freetown for Wilberforce on a Saturday afternoon was the biggest transportation hurdle I had ever experienced. So I decided to write about my struggle to get to the prize-giving service.

Before Miss Benjamin returned the essays, she sat down and picked up the one at the top of her pile.

"I'm going to read you the best essay in the class." She struggled to contain herself.

The class followed suit, shuffling our books and whispering animatedly into each other's ears.

Then, when the class finally settled down, I heard Miss Benjamin read a description of my agony of waking up early on Saturday morning to finish my chores so that I would be allowed to attend the prize-giving service, my struggle to press my uniform with a charcoal iron that wouldn't heat up, the intensity of the sun upon leaving the house, and my rush back into the house for a handkerchief. She read the metaphors and similes I used to describe my walk to Clock Tower; the envy I didn't allow to settle as I peeked into private cars and taxicabs carrying MGHS girls snuggled next to their parents; the mixture of sweat and tears that swelled up my eyes after the third bus that did not say Congo Cross; my steadfast vow that "I will not be seen in a *poda poda*. Not in my Wesleyan uniform," even as the clock's long hand was already on five, and the short hand on three, knowing the service was to start at four, and I was still in the East End. She showed my knuckles firmly on my straw hat as I made the decision to walk down Kissy Street and on to Wilberforce Street, until I reached the bus depot in the middle of town. How fulfilling it was when finally, I saw a bus marked Congo Cross!

When Miss Benjamin reached the end of the essay, the class was silent.

Even I, did not know how to respond as she handed me back my essay and said, "I'm very proud of you. You should consider yourself a proud Wesleyan."

How a Boy Crossed the Highest Mountain

Despite the leather cord Attatie put around my waist, I had a boyfriend, a stocky, shiney-eyed Westender whom I let kiss me three times a year. The rest of the time, we exchanged love letters written on pages off our exercise books. "In the garden of love where two roses meet and shall never die." And I would respond with "Roses are red, violets are blue, I don't sleep at night cause I'm thinking of you." Often, his letters expressed "an undying love" and a readiness to "cross the highest mountain and the deepest ocean to reach you."

The letters were hand delivered. As the group of Technical School boys walked past our school driveway on their way to the bus stop, Sammy's friend would slip the folded paper in my hand. I read it on the bus, to exclamations and cheers from my classmates, and later, to Glynis and Melissa on our walk home from the bus stop. A day or two after, I would signal to the friend that I had a reply.

The kisses came during the all secondary schools sports competition, the Prize-giving and the Thanksgiving services. Amidst the thumping cheers of the final races, Sammy and I made our way under the bleachers and joined the orgy of boys and girls drooling into each other's mouths. Sammy drew me close to his sturdy frame, placed my arm around his waist, held my head up to his mouth, and drained a volume of spittle down my throat. I swallowed it all, proud I could say I was a woman, not a house child.

Content with ourselves, we held hands under the diming daylight, through the dips and rises of Savage Street on the walk home.

"Did you receive my letter?" he said in a voice I thought manly.

"Yes," I whispered, bringing a finger to my lips. "Did you receive mine?

"Yes."

We walked in silence for another ten minutes or so, until we reached the narrow shoulders of Sanders Street.

"Where do you live?" he said.

"Leah Street."

"Where's that?" He turned to face me.

"In the East End." I stared into a car's headlight.

"Oh." He covered his mouth and swiped down an imaginary beard.

"Where do you live?" I said.

"Not far from here." He pointed into the darkness in front of him. "On Wellington Street."

We were at the junction of Sandas and Siaka Stevens Streets.

"Oh." I was now looking inside of a taxi slowing down a bit too close to us.

I always carried with me the fear of Attatie stepping out of a taxi-cab to drag me home. I untied Sammy's grip of my hand and pretended to be scratching my head, my attention focused on building a story about why I wasn't rushing home after the competitions had ended, and what I was doing strolling next to a boy.

The taxi came to a stop, the woman came out and crossed the road.

I held Sammy's hand again. We reached the slope where Wellington Street joined Siaka Stevens Street.

"That's my house." He pointed down Wellington Street. "The low, gray one with lights on."

"Oh," I said.

We walked on. We reached Walpole Street and stood in front of the cotton tree spread, waiting to cross over to the Courthouse.

"I've never been to the East End before."

"Oh." I noticed he was making no move to cross the road. "Oh," I repeated.

"My parents are home." He already had his back to me. "I'll write you another letter."

Mrs. Josephine Lamin

"No group has ever completed form five of the commercial stream without suspension," Mrs. Lamin leaned forward on the table, her enormous breasts taking up a good part of the desk.

Her dictation books occupied the rest of the space.

"Sometimes it's a few girls. Other times, it's the entire class that gets suspended for at least one week." She sounded gleeful. "In my ten or so years as form teacher of this class, there's even been one expulsion."

I believed she was bluffing, trying to put ice on our collective swagger as we commenced our final year of compulsory hair braiding and school uniform.

We were her captive audience. She was not only our form teacher, but she taught us shorthand, typewriting, and office duties. The fifteen or so of us listened to her all day whining and indoctrinating us with unsolicited advice about the outside world. "The outside world is too large to accept all of you. Believe you me, it will have to crush some of you."

She complained about the amount of money expatriate teachers received for doing what she called *fart* and incapable of reaching us the way local teachers did.

"I will not leave my enemy's child to their mercies," she would say. "That porridge-hearted upbringing that spoil children."

In Shorthand class, we took one dictation after the other, and typed them out in Typing class. Her dictations were all letters from one manager in London to another in Essex or Lancaster, or another British city. There were never letters from managers in the country where we were going to be working. Sometimes, she asked a girl to

279

read back her dictation before Typing class. "Theodora, please read back what you wrote," she would say, as she applied lipstick in front of us. If Theodora had too gaps in her reading, Mrs. Lamin would rant about how dangerously unprepared we all were for the outside world. She would follow up with reasons why "it will ruin your reputation to sleep with the boss," and Moronike would roll her eyes.

One day, out of nowhere, Mrs. Lamin advised us to "never accept the first marriage proposal that comes your way,"

Mrs. Lamin's words made sense to us only when she was in the room. The minute her back was turned, we released repressed giggles.

On those days that Papa picked me up from school, we gave Mrs. Lamin a ride. She would sit in the front seat with Papa and listen to him narrate stories about his childhood friendship with her husband. The two men were distant relatives whose relationship waned after Mr. Lamin left for England. It didn't matter what they were talking about, though. Mrs. Lamin always found a way to bring the conversation to me. She told Papa all the terrible things that happened to young African girls who went to England. She complained about the culture shock, the weather, the loneliness, the naivete, which she said affected girls much more than it did boys. As she got off the car at the junction of Kissy Road and Magazine Cut, she would repeat the same song. "I have taught her enough skills to work right here in Freetown and earn a decent salary."

Face-to-face with the Outside World

On the morning of my interview, I got out of Papa's Peugeot in front the Ministry of Agriculture building. A mob was scattered around the foot of a long expanse of rickety stairs, trying to buy food.

"Hurry up, mammy," one of them hollered. "I'm almost late for work."

Another yelled for more *akara* on his bread, and another pushed an older man who had cut in front of him. Each one howled above the woman's faint, stuttering calls for patience. Others stood around eating breakfast out of old newspapers.

I managed to stifle the temptation to turn back and ask Papa to accompany me up the stairs. It was my first time in an office building where I might be working, and the curious eyes made me uncomfortable.

I gripped the straps of my handbag, steadied myself.

"Young lady, who are you here to see?" a voice called behind me.

I turned around to see a man bundling up a soiled newspaper. There were several doors in front of me, any of which could be Miss Olive's office.

"I'm here to see the confidential secretary to the permanent secretary," I said, making sure I spoke in English.

"She's my boss," he said in a sober tone, and threw the newspaper ball out the window. "Follow me."

The sounds of someone shelling peanuts told me I had reached Miss Olive's office. The sign on the door said *Confidential Secretary*, but the office looked more like a roomy box for filing cabinets.

"Attatie told me to come and see you," I said.

"Come in." She gestured for me to sit. "Look how nicely you're growing."

The chair to which she motioned was stacked with piles of withered vanilla folders marked *Confidential*.

"Just put those on the floor," she said.

My mind went to Mrs. Lamin in Office Duties, so I put my palms under the folders as if I were holding overripe mangos and stooped down to lay them on the floor close to the cabinets.

The only window in the office was a square casement with four rectangular glass louvers that opened into another office. Miss Olive made a manifest effort to press the louvers close before beginning to speak.

"They're looking for a secretary in the Land Resources office, and I've—"

The piercing shrill of the office bell sent her jumping out of her chair. She opened one of the glass louvers and peeped through it.

Then she whisked around to tell me, "He's getting ready to go out," as she was pulling down the hem of her dress. "I will be able to take you to the Land Survey office and back before he returns."

I sensed she was referring to the permanent secretary, so I nodded.

She squeezed herself between the typewriter desk and a filing cabinet to reach the door. After she was gone, I consoled myself with the reminder that I was only going to work in Freetown for a year. Papa had promised me I will go to England afterwards. In the meantime, I promised myself the I will not work for a man like Miss Olive's boss, even if he had a position above permanent secretary.

Miss Olive stopped to greet several colleagues on the way to the Land Resources building. The office campus looked more like a bazaar than an office, with more food hawkers on the corridors, selling boiled corn, people selling merchandise like shoes and bags, while others just hung around idly. You had to look hard to tell the employees from the traders and the visitors.

Dr. Terry's office reeked of alcohol and stale cigar. Large maps carpeted his table—some in thick long folds the length of the table. Others, in flat spreads. He appeared to have been making colored markings on different spots on the map before we walked in. Tall bookcases stalked the walls on each side of him, carrying books with titles like *Tropical Agriculture* and *Land Resources*. He was tall, with broad shoulders. As Miss Olive and I entered the room, he lifted his head for only a moment, before returning to his maps.

"Yes, yes, come in." He motioned for us to sit.

"This is the secretary I spoke to you about," Miss Olive said, as we were sitting down.

When he lifted his head, a pair of bloodshot eyes made a ruler-straight line to the unbuttoned part of my blouse. Then he squeezed his gaze so directly into mine, and I saw an image of Mrs. Barry in Office Duties class.

"Tangling up yourselves in relationships with older men will only destroy your future."

I had not even had a school relationship with someone my own age, let alone an office relationship with someone my father's age.

I dropped my eyes and let his gaze fall on my forehead.

"She types seventy words per minute," Miss Olive said. "And her shorthand speed is a hundred words per minute."

"Whew!" he whistled, now paying attention to Miss Olive.

It was obvious he was attempting to lighten the moment, but neither Miss Olive nor I were lighthearted. So he took his gaze off Miss Olive and returned them to my chest. But now, when he looked at me, his eyes were cold and apathetic, as if the information about my shorthand and typing speeds had suddenly flattened the perk of my eighteen-year-old chest. The relative warmth with which he had received us was disappearing. Miss Olive had thrown cold water on his pants. Now, she went on to freeze that water.

"You know her father at the Ministry of Lands," Miss Olive said in a dry tone. "You went to Prince of Wales School with him."

"Yes, yes, you told me." Then for a minute or two, he busied himself drawing circles on the map. "My assistant is out of the office this week." He brought up his head slowly to look at the space between Miss Olive and me. "We will discuss the matter on his return."

It was not his words about the job, but those of Mrs. Lamin that were ringing in my ears when I stepped out of Dr. Terry's office: "Believe you me, it will have to crush some of you."

Outside of Dr. Terry's office, I decided that even if I was offered the job, I would not accept it. I did not have to work, anyway. There was no pressure on me to contribute to my living expenses. Had Mrs. Lamin not cut into my dream, I would be in England by now.Papa was comfortable having me at home, and Attatie would rather I spend my growing-up time helping at the rice store.

Then we passed by a small room on the east side of the Land Survey office, where two women sat at typewriters, and my mood lightened up.

"Theodora!" I shouted. "

Memuna!" She jumped out of her seat to hug me.

We had survived Mrs. Lamin together. *It'll be like school. We'll be strong together.*

On the afternoon of my first day at the Land Survey office, one of the messengers came to say Dr. Terry wanted me in his office to take dictation for a letter. The office was an old colonial-style building with a long veranda separated into east and west wings. The west wing housed the office manager, messengers, and secretaries. And on the East were the larger and more luxurious offices of Dr. Terry and his deputy, a Swedish expatriate. When the directors needed to see a staff from the west wing, they rang a bell for a messenger.

I got my note and pencil and went eastward, excited to be on my way to taking my first real dictation. Theodora had calmed my fears by saying Dr. Terry was more interested in his bottle than in women, so I figured I had nothing to worry about.

The messenger, a twenty-year trouper of the civil service, walked alongside me, trying to make conversation. Or, since he worked in an office, collect information.

"I can tell this is your first job," he said.

I did not respond. My mind was on my real dictation. I was used to taking dictations read by a teacher—dictations I strove to get right, only to get a good point for my report card. Now, I would have to type a letter that will be going to a real person.

"You cannot be older than eighteen," the messenger said.

My age is none of your business.

I was wondering if Dr. Terry would use words I had not come across before.

As soon as Attatie told me I had the job, I began drilling words connected with the job—words like *agriculture, soil, land, rice, resources.* After I found out that most of the land resources work was conducted in provincial areas, I had to create my own shorthand strokes for places like Port Loko and Kambia, for words like savanna and mangrove, and even Sierra Leone.

"Is it true you went to the same school as that flippant Theodora?"

I will not hold familiar conversations with an office messenger.

He stopped moving. "Do you want me to stand outside the door?"

I knew exactly what he meant. But I remembered Theodora's words.

"No," I replied. "I'm going to take dictation for a letter."

I ignored his chuckle.

Dr. Terry wasn't sure what I was doing in his office.

"You sent for me," I reminded him.

"Oh, yes, yes. Sit down." He rubbed his chin.

I sat on a chair opposite his desk, and he leaned forward on the desk, placed his elbows on the table, and squeezed his face in his hands.

"Are you liking the office so far?" He sounded friendly.

"Oh yes," I said. "Theodora and I went to the same school, you know. I feel very comfortable here."

He pushed his face close enough for me to sniffle out the smell of alcohol.

"What about me?" he said, his eyes dimming. "Do you feel comfortable with me?"

I started to bow my head in embarrassment. I knew he was not talking about father-daughter comfort. I thought of the messenger's request to stand outside the door, but did not regret rejecting it. Mrs. Lamin had prepared me for this.

"From the first day in your place of work," she had said once, "your actions will determine your accommodation into the outside world."

I will have Mrs. Lamin's support, whatever I decide to do.

"I feel more comfortable with Theodora." I jerked my head to stare into his eyes. "We are of the same age, and—"

He caught the fire in my voice.

"Take this." He threw the letter at me.

He had already scribbled a memorandum only a few lines long, with words written, scratched, and rewritten, on top of one another.

I said nothing to Theodora, nor to the senior secretary, Mrs. Denton, who was a short, thick woman with puffed cheekbones that made her look like she was always moping. Although I could tell the experienced Mrs. Denton suspected something, all she did was ask if I needed help with my dictation. Then, without waiting for me to respond, took the letter from my hand and motioned for me to sit at my desk, while she began helping me make out Dr. Terry's handwriting.

I finished typing the letter, sure that I had done a good job. Instead of taking it to him to look over and sign, I gave it to the messenger to take to him. I was going to put my foot down on day one!

It was common knowledge in the office that Simon Gerber, Dr. Terry's deputy, did the work of himself and Dr. Terry, without malice. Mrs. Denton said he was so happy to be living in a warm climate, and he could not bring himself to complain about anything. He was the first to arrive at the office in the morning, and usually the last to leave.

A cactus-sized, cigar-smoking Swiss, Dr. Gerber seldom used the office messengers. He hopped back and forth from one wing to the other, fogging up the corridors with cigar smoke. He went out of his way to be genial, beseeching everyone to call him Simon.

Initially, I strained to concede. The imaginary British bosses to whom we typed letters at school were a Mr. Pendleton or a Dr. Watson. But Theodora already called him Simon, so I followed suit, even though the older staff, like Mrs. Denton and the office manager, insisted on calling him Dr. Gerber.

Once, Simon invited the entire west wing staff into his office to look at infrared pictures of what he called, *your beautiful virgin landscape.* Mrs. Denton and the office manager said they had too much work to do. But Theodora and I, who acted as though we were still in secondary school, jumped at the opportunity to do anything we considered fun.

"Look how beautiful your country is." Simon handed me a picture that looked like someone had spilled red ink on the vegetation.

I was sitting on one of the chairs in front of him, and Theodora had perched herself on the chair's arm.

"Yes, it is beautiful." I passed the picture to Theodora.

She snatched it from my hand, and after only a passing glace, returned it the table. With each picture of trees, forests, mountains, low-
lands, all painted red, Simon defended the acquisition of an infrared
camera to capture what he called, *the essence* of the country's landscape,
and enable us all, with his help, to do great things with our resources.
I wondered if he had spatted with Dr. Terry over purchase of the
camera.

Neither Theodora nor I had been schooled in a manner that would
have piqued our interest, even vaguely, in our country's landscape or
natural resources. It was no different with the older staff that had used
work to escape the viewing. I was interested only in growing up fast
enough for my parents to allow me to go to England on my own.

Theodora, whose father, the only breadwinner of the family, died
when she was in secondary school, was interested only in activities that
would help her provide for her mother and younger brother. So we
both feigned interest and awe and agreed with everything Simon said
about our land resources, until Theodora's attention became divided
between the office ceiling and the pictures. Soon, she was snatching the
pictures from my hand, only to slam them on Simon's table.

Then we came to a picture of Simon in a bowler hat and camera
atop a high peak.

"This is Mount Bintumani," he said.

He had piqued Theodora's interest. "We read about it in geography
lesson!" she said. "It's the highest mountain in Sierra Leone."

Other than that, she didn't remember any details of the mountain,
and neither did I.

"Beautiful! Beautiful!" Theodora kept repeating.

Simon did not appear to read the sarcasm in Theodora's voice. He
put down his cigar and looked up with great expectation.

"Why don't we go and climb Mount Bintumani together."

I became worried right away. Theodora had gotten up too slowly
from the chair's arm. I feared she was going to leave the room in dis-
gust, and maybe throw the picture in the dustbin along the way. But
she just walked around the room, as if trying to convince herself that
Simon had not asked her to go on a non-official trip with him.

I thought it would be fun climbing a mountain over six-thousand-
feet high. My only ventures outside of Freetown were a school trip

around the peninsula, and the health trip I made with Attatie to Port Loko when I was around six or seven.

"OK!" I replied, trying to build up excitement.

Without Theodora's input, Simon and I agreed on a departure date two Saturdays away.

"What time shall I pick you up." Simon played with the cigar in his mouth.

Theodora's joyless countenance had done little to abate his enthusiasm.

"You'll pick up Memuna first," she said in a dryly.

"Mm…yes," I said. "The same time we leave for work, eight o'clock," I said.

I figured I would tell my parents I was going to work.

"Eight o'clock is too early for me," Theodora said.

"In that case, we'll let you know, Simon," I said.

"And you'll give me your addresses." He jerked his head from me to Theodora.

We agreed, knowing full well we were not going to do any such thing.

As soon as we returned to our office, Theodora my elbow and pushed me toward Mrs. Denton's desk.

"Tell her what you've just done."

I was going to explain the entire thing to Mrs. Denton, when one of the office messengers walked in, followed by Simon's chauffeur. Theodora understood that I was not going to talk about the proposed trip in front of Simon's chauffeur or the messenger, so she followed my move and returned to her desk while Mrs. Denton busied herself with the chauffeur and messenger.

The Land Resources office was the last of a series of dilapidated government buildings on a hill that once provided refuge for British forces fighting local tribes. There was plenty of opportunity to grind the office rumor mill as staff from the different offices passed in front of our building on their way up and down Tower Hill.

The second the office was free of messengers and chauffeurs, Theodora got up.

"Missus Denton," she moaned. "I'm not going to be seen in the same car with a white man."

"But it will not look that bad with the two of us in the car," I said.

"Missus Denton." Theodora moved toward the senior secretary's desk. "I will never put myself in a position where people will call me a prostitute."

I got up. "But what people will say should not decide who we go around with."

"That's your life, not mine," Theodora said. "As for me," she pointed toward her chest, "no white man is picking me up in a car in front of my house, in broad daylight, for all the neighbors to see."

"Then he'll pick you up at night." I smiled.

But Theodora was not joking. She spun around to return to her desk.

"What's so wrong with driving in a car with a white man who's your workmate?" I said. "Why shouldn't I ride about town with a white man, if that's what I want, without worrying about people thinking he was taking me to the nearest hotel room?

Theodora did not respond. Neither did Mrs. Denton.

But I angered Theodora even more when I said, "Even if that was the case, why should I care what others think?"

She banged a fist on her typewriter. "That's it Missus Denton. Memuna is too flighty for my comfort. I have nothing else to say to her. I'm not going anywhere with a white man."

I might have been flighty in Theodora's eyes, but I was turning nineteen. After years of listening to Granny talk about what *we* did and did not do, after the everyday struggle to emulate Attatie's *good* people, after the levelheadedness I had exhibited, maybe I was beginning to fill up. I had completed secondary school and spent an additional year at the Technical Institute, doing what Papa called, *growing up a bit more*. I still lived with my parents, but I was now working and earning a salary. Most importantly, I had been accepted into a commercial school in England, and I was making plans to live in a hostel. *Soon, I will be making my own decisions, and going and coming on my own terms.*

I was like done rice bread. I was beginning to shed the banana leaves that had been used to hold me together in the oven. I was baked now and eager to set a path of my own. *I will select friends and acquaintances of my choice, not ones imposed on me by my parents' history.*

But even as I stood defiantly in front of Mrs. Denton's desk, I was already searching for the best words with which to make my case to Attatie. She was stitched together with the same fabric as Theodora and Mrs. Denton. *She will worry that the neighbors, especially those to whom she has made clear, live below her station, will revel in what they will see as her daughter falling below even the level of the Idris girls.*

"Mrs. Denton," I said, "I'm sure my father did, at one time or another, go on a social outing with his white boss."

Mrs. Denton let out a derisive chortle. "For Jesus Christ's sake! You're living a light life."

"What's wrong with a light life?"

"People are not going to judge a young girl the same way they do a young man."

"I do not care about how people will judge me. So long as my intentions are honorable, I'll do what I want."

"I will not sit back and let you throw away a decent upbringing because of ideas that do not belong to us."

Silence followed her outburst. Theodora typed vigorously, and I stood like concrete at the center of the office.

Mrs. Denton pointed a finger at me. "What if, on your way to the mountains, you get into an accident, and all three of you—Theodora, Simon—die."

"We die!" I said.

Theodora hissed.

"Yes, you die." Mrs. Denton was trying to keep her calm. "But... but...but have you considered the miles between your honorable intentions and what people will say?"

"What people will say! What people will say!" I returned to my desk. "Mrs. Denton, I'm tired of hearing about what people will say. I'm tired of doing what others expect of me!" I shouted, from behind my typewriter. "What about what I believe? What about what I want? I want to climb Mount Bintumani with a colleague."

"Who do you believe will defend you!" she said. "Who do you think will defend you after you're gone, against charges of greedy young girls, even with good jobs, running after white men for money?"

"You will defend me, Mrs. Denton, because you know my intentions."

"I swear in the name of my children," she pointed a finger to the ceiling, "I will not lift a finger to defend your disgraced soul."

As angry as I was at Mrs. Denton's words, I could not help thinking about my mother trying to explain my actions to *good* people like the Englishes. I thought of her succumbing to the realization that she had raised a daughter not much different, after all, from the Idris girl who had descended into prostitution to feed her three children. I thought of her struggling, still, to put blocks of difference between her educated daughter and those unfortunate girls from up-country who often ended up baby mothers to a series of white men like Simon Gerber.

It took a day or two for our heads to cool down. I was perched on one side of Mrs. Denton's desk, and Theodora stood on the other side.

"How about we just let him sit in front of your house and honk his car horn until sunset?" Theodora said.

"How about I tell him my parents are opposed to the trip?" I replied.

"He'll think you're still a child and shouldn't be working in an office," Mrs. Denton said.

Finally, without a charge on our collective conscience, without concern for personal honor, we settled on chicanery.

On the eve of the planned trip, about thirty minutes before knock of time, Mrs. Denton sent one of the messengers on an errand that in reality was to make sure Simon was in his office working. We had let none of them onto our plan, for we knew word would certainly reach Simon through his chauffeur.

I crossed my handbag over my chest and held hands with Theodora as we headed toward the corridor. We were taking our first furtive steps down the stairs, into the parking lot, when a voice said.

"Good afternoon, Miss Sillah. Good afternoon, Miss Mansfield." A clerk from the ministry was coming down the slope, shouting as though his bus fare home depended on him greeting us.

Before Theodora and I could begin gesticulating *quiet* with our hands over our mouths, Simon was running toward us, pointing a cigar to his watch.

"What time tomorrow? What time?"

Theodora, for once, looked genuinely sad. I was searching for a hole in the ground to bury myself. I wished Mrs. Denton would come out of her office and tell us what to do next.

"Sorry, Simon, I'm busy tomorrow," was the lie I came up with.

For weeks, I was unable to look into Simon's bottle-green eyes. I typed his letters very quickly so he wouldn't hang around—as was his habit—long enough to start a conversation that might lead to the Bintumani trip.

One afternoon, I summoned the courage to put my face through his office window to say hello. He grinned widely and jumped from his chair to beckon me in. It surprised me that he showed no malice. I promised to come back when I was less busy.

The part of me that wanted to indulge him had been checked. I needed time to make up my mind about the distance I was going to put for now, between me and the person I wanted to be tomorrow.

One morning, Simon's chauffeur came into our office and announced that Simon's family was coming to Freetown. It was a rainy morning, and the secretarial pool was just settling down after the damp, stuffy air usually left behind by the rain was beginning to dissipate. The three office chauffeurs were hanging around in our office: Simon's chauffeur; the older man who drove the utility Land Rover; and Dr. Terry's chauffeur, who was more a general office driver since Dr. Terry didn't want to be driven around town by anyone but himself.

It had soon become common knowledge in the offices, thanks to the messengers and chauffeurs, that Dr. Terry spent most of his office hours at a bar, and his Swiss deputy was in the process of building a house for his chauffeur's sister, a girl who used to frequent hotel bars, and was now the mother of Simon's newborn son.

"He got a letter. She's coming with the children." The chauffeur himself appeared unable to believe what he had just said.

Mrs. Denton's mouth dropped. Theodora joked about calling the newspapers, and everyone laughed, except the chauffeur. He looked as though he had just fallen on rocks, his jaws smashed in. He had received the perks that came with the title of perceived brother-in-law of the office expatriate. He had been able to bring into employment, many of his friends and relatives. With Mrs. Gerber coming, his sister and nephew would naturally be abandoned— probably until his sister could secure another expatriate. His pocket would get emptier and emptier during that wait, especially if it was a long one.

The Gerber family came. I was the one who typed the memorandum, three or four months later, informing the permanent secretary that the mosquitoes in Sierra Leone, the weather, and all accompanying tropical diseases, had launched an attack on poor Mrs. Gerber's health. As for the children, they were unable to find in Freetown, schools at the level to which they were accustomed in Switzerland.

So the chauffeur regained the security of his position, and now spent even less time at the office, and more attending to the transportation needs of his sister.

Jumia and I strolled into Simon's office on a slack afternoon a few weeks later to chat. With the chauffeur no longer frequent in the office, there was a dearth of information on Simon's private life, which by now was a mini soap opera.

He bolted from his chair to receive us, offered us some cold drinks, and hopped from the fridge to the table to open the drinks. I got a pint of Vimto, and Theodora got Coca Cola. Simon got himself a Sprite, went back to his chair and put both feet on the table.

"Are you missing your family?" I stole looks at Theodora.

He squinted for merely a fraction of a second, then picked up his cigar. He sucked in, laid back on the chair and puffed out the smoke. Then he flashed a rascal grin before responding, by way of complaint about the tropical weather's assault on his wife's health.

"You must be sad that your sons were not able to stay," Theodora said.

"I will be fine," he said, reddening a bit, then taking another puff at his cigar. "This is Salone," he said, calling Sierra Leone by its local name. He had already spent two of his five year contract in Salone.

He pulled out his drawer and took out pictures. He showed us a picture of his wife in a bikini in the backyard pool—a blond with a short face like Simon himself. Then there were pictures of his two sons in swimming trunks, both with Simon's green eyes. The next picture was that of the chauffeur's sister, in the same beach chair on which his wife sat in the earlier picture. She was holding their new son. Next to her was an older child. He, too, was of mixed race, but too old to be Simon's child. He looked seven or eight.

"Will you take them to Switzerland with you when you leave?" I said.

He reddened. "I'm building them a house."

He had learned the custom. He had learned that Muslim men could take as many wives as their pockets permit, and Christian men could build houses for their surpluses. He would live comfortably in Salone until his time came, his contract up, when he would depart and leave mother and child with a house. He would have done the decent thing, according to many in the country. He would have done better than his Scottish predecessor, the father of the older child in the picture.

The Ferry to England

The engine of Papa's old Peugeot panted lazily in the garage. Sun rays streaked the cars waiting outside our house. The Idris family put a tray of mangos on the steps of their gate. Glynis waved to me as she returned from church with her family. A light wind hissed past the dining room window. Uncle sang a loud hymn from his porch. Miss Nanette held quiet consul with Sissy Mary under her apple tree.

The family came. Aunty Mariama and Aunty Fatmata had never traveled outside of Freetown, but they brought all the advice they said a young girl needed to be successful in England: stay home with your books and make no friends. Granny sent a chastity beed, and Grandma Ndamba, from Sackville Street, brought a sheep horn for my handbag, against every calamity that exists in the white man's land.

Papa had cleaned out the Peugeot. Mohammed killed two fowls, and Attatie stepped into the kitchen to prepare the rice and chicken stew for our lunch. Amie, Fatmata, and Hassana helped her in the kitchen, and Abassy washed dishes.

I inched one foot after the other over a timid white goat someone had brought before dawn. It was my last step from our house at Leah Street to England. Pa said I would leap over every bad fortune that befell me in the white man's land.

The ferry trembled violently, coughed sooty smoke, and set off. Passengers began getting out of their cars for the upper deck. Attatie held my hand like I was a toddler on spilled okra soup. Aunty Fatmata took the other. We climbed rusty soaked steps, against the seawater splashing on our faces. Before I could sit, Attatie removed her head tie and busied herself swiping water off my face and handbag. She flapped water off my jacket as if a mosquito was sitting on it.

"We don't want you going to England in soaked clothes," she said, even though the splashes had only reached my face.

She had dressed me up like the women on British television shows. I wore a fawn, long-sleeved crepe suit complete with collar and breast pocket, and a pencil skirt. A Queen Elizabeth type handbag dangled on my right arm.

"You look like an English woman already." She installed me next to her on the ferry bench, like a cargo marked *fragile*.

My sisters scrambled to take seats close to me, but Attatie and Aunty Fatmata had already flanked me. They took seats on the other side of Attatie and Aunty Fatmata. Papa sat on the bench behind us. Mohammed and Abassy left to get drinks.

"Your last pint of Vimto," Mohammed said, as if Vimtos had not come from England.

Papa lit a cigarette behind us.

"Behave yourself over there." Attatie was now playing with my curls. "Keep your eyes down so you can see your nose."

I promised I would.

"Look at her," Aunty Fatmata said. "Already, she looks like a white woman."

My mother agreed, proudly. She opened my handbag and closed it again.

"You have your traveler's checks, right?" She tucked the straps of my handbag inside my elbow. "Make sure you don't lose those checks."

I assured her I would not lose them.

"And remember to walk fast when you get there." It was a rebuke. "Like those women we see on television."

My sisters giggled behind us.

"I always walk fast," I said.

"Yes, but walk faster. You have to be wide awake in those countries."

I said I would be wide awake.

"And when you go out, always hold your handbag like this." She pointed to the straps she'd inserted inside the crook of my elbow. "That's how the women we see on television hold their bags."

Did she say go out? My mind lit up. What possibilities awaited me! I was going to be leaving on my own in London. *There will be no Papa or Attatie to monitor my movements. I'll have all the boyfriends I want.*

"Be a good woman." Aunty Fatmata read my mind.

I did not answer.

My parents were sending me to England, against their better judgment. I was aware of that. I was also aware that since turning twenty, I was now a young woman. The year I spent earning a salary, exposed to the outside world, had enlightened me. I was on my way to the place that had wrought men like Professor Palmer and Mr. English, women like Miss Fenella, Mrs. Jarrett, and Mrs. Collier. But I doubted my parents guessed that, even before I set foot on foreign soil, even before I was flying, I had stepped far enough from the narrow space in which I grew up, and I was already moving beyond the fabricated classes, beyond the constructed *we.*

I still think Aunty Jennifer and Cassandra played a role in quietening my parents' worry about sending me to England. The Abrahams had moved from their ambassador position in England to another in the US. Cassandra and siblings had remained in boarding school in England. I was going to stay at a girls' hostel in Earls Court, but Aunty Jennifer told my parents not to worry.

"Cassandra lives in London," she said. "They can take care of each other."

Cassandra promised to chaperon me around London. The family had been on vacation in Freetown, so Papa booked me on the same flight as Cassandra, who was going back to school ahead of the rest of her family.

"But where's Cassandra?" I had become tired of the fuss.

I stood up to look around.

"You might fall. Oh, be careful. You don't want to fall when you're going to England."

Even my sisters joined in the commotion so intense, nearby passengers stopped to pay attention to us.

I quickly sat back. "Have you seen Cassandra?"

Attatie turned to Papa.

"It's only a few minutes past noon," Papa said, cigarette in mouth. "It's an overnight flight. She might be taking a later ferry."

Mohammed arrived with the Vimto, and I almost emptied the pint on my first sip.

The voices rose again:

"You'll have to use the toilet if you continue drinking like that."

"You'll soil your clothes."

"You should wait until you get to England to use the toilet. You don't want to use our dirty airport toilets."

A violent tremor, and we trembled on our seats. Mohammed pronounced us arrived at Lungi. We returned to our cars for the scenic ride to the airport—half-clothed, bulk-bellied children waving to us from mud huts; women fanning rice; and old men on hammocks.

Airport laborers fought to carry our luggage. Passengers yelled at relatives to hurry with one thing or another. Peddlers shoved their goods in front of us, and skinny, white airline staff fanned themselves profusely against the sultry air.

"Let's look for someone we know to take care of the bags."

"No, let's go straight to the counter and make sure she doesn't have excess."

"No, let's find some good seats first. The airport is crowded."

"No, let's go find somewhere we can settle down to eat first."

In the end, Aunty Fatmata carried the food basket to the side of the building to look for somewhere we could sit down to eat, while the rest of us entered the airport.

Papa took my ticket and Mohammed held on to my luggage.

The rest of us joined Aunty Fatmata under an almond tree. We sat on large boulders and brought out the food dishes. Attatie sat next to me, opened the drinks, and distributed a pint to each person.

She relieved me of my handbag while I ate. She opened and closed it several times, making sure my travelers' checks were still in there.

I finished eating and began to sweat. I was dressed for a London spring weather, not the ninety degrees of Lungi. Attatie began fanning me with her head tie.

"If I die before you return, I am counting on you to take care of your sisters."

It came out of nowhere, but it wasn't the first time she had made the solemn pronouncement.

I told her I would.

"Mohammed and Amie…" She examined the distance in front of her. She had picked up her plate of food but had not touched the spoon. "They're older than you, but—"

A laborer in an under-vest passed in front of us.

"Why's he at the airport in his undervest?" she barked.

I told her I believed something needed to be done about men coming to the airport in their under-vests. She agreed vehemently.

"Mohammed and Amie," she continued, "they often do not put their heads down enough to see their noses." She looked into the distance again. "They're older, but from what I can see…"

She stopped to shout at a young man that was about to pee on a tree in front of us. I told her I strongly believed men peeing outside the airport should be outlawed.

"That's why I'll miss you," she said. "You see with my eyes."

She brought the side edges of her wrapper to her eyes.

"You are the first one to leave the family to go and study in England."

I told her not to cry. That I would be back in three years.

"Maybe this is the last we time we will be seeing each other." She blew her nose. Loudly! "Make sure you offer frequent sacrifices in my name after I'm gone." She wiped her eyes again. "Do not turn into a white woman in England."

I promised I would not turn into a white woman.

"Do not forget that we raised you a Muslim, and that…Cassandra!" she hollered.

It was as if a magic wand had just erased all her fears.

"We've been looking all over for you."

Cassandra stood in front of me and cracked up.

"You're dressed like that, going to London?" she said, between fits of guffaws.

"That's how women dress in England," Attatie said, trying to pull me up by the elbow.

I refused to stand up.

It hadn't been necessary to discuss clothing with Cassandra after Mother had already given the fabric for my suit to Aunty Ijatu, with instructions on how to sew it. Cassandra usually wore pencil skirts, but I had never seen her in those crepe jackets British housewives on television wore. I remained seated on the boulder admiring Cassandra's sleeveless blouse and unbuttoned chest. She listened respectfully to Attatie make her case for my dress, but she was unable to take her eyes off me.

Luckily, Papa came and told Cassandra to go check in her luggage. She did and returned promptly to ask,

"You're not going to hold your handbag like that in London, are you?"

Attatie replied that every English woman held her handbag straps in her elbow dent.

"You see the way I hold my bag," Cassandra managed to say, between giggles.

She was grabbing a black crocodile clutch bag under her armpits.

"This is the way you hold your handbag in London," she said.

Attatie's mouth dropped. She looked around her for support, for someone to help her convince this know-nothing child about how women held their bags in London.

"But that's how you hold your bag at the Bombay Street market," she said finally, throwing her arms around.

"Aunty Amie," Cassandra chuckled, "for every pickpocket you have at the Bombay Street market, there are a thousand in London."

My mother had to sit down.

"Aaaaaaaaaaaye. Subuan'allai!"

Her recovery took more than a few minutes, but it came.

"Come with me." She pulled me by the arm.

In the bathroom, she removed the travelers checks from my handbag and plied each one once—about ten of them. She unbuttoned my jacket and divided the checks into each of my breasts.

"We'll show them we know how to deal with bad people over there."

She patted both breasts to make sure the checks did not fall, returned my handbag straps to my elbow and walked me out of the room.

***

There was a stocky barb-haired girl in the boarding room. She helped herself to the airport telephone, over which she made several conversations in affected English. Then she got up and walked around,